Canine Enrichment
for the Real World
Workbook

Allie Bender, CDBC and Emily Strong, CDBC

Wenatchee, Washington U.S.A.

Canine Enrichment for the Real World Workbook
Allie Bender and Emily Strong

Dogwise Publishing
A Division of Direct Book Service, Inc.
403 South Mission Street, Wenatchee, Washington 98801
1-509-663-9115, 1-800-776-2665
www.dogwisepublishing.com / info@dogwisepublishing.com
© 2022 Allie Bender and Emily Strong

Interior: Lindsay Davisson
Cover design: Jesus Cordero

Limits of Liability and Disclaimer of Warranty:
The author and publisher shall not be liable in the event of incidental or consequential damages in connection with, or arising out of, the furnishing, performance, or use of the instructions and suggestions contained in this book.

Library of Congress Cataloging-in-Publication Data

Names: Bender, Allie, 1980- author. | Strong, Emily, 1979- author.

Title: Canine enrichment for the real world : workbook / Allie Bender, CDBC
and Emily Strong, CDBC.

Description: Wenatchee, Washington U.S.A. : Dogwise Publishing, [2022]

Identifiers: LCCN 2022026363 | ISBN 9781617813245 (paperback)

Subjects: LCSH: Dogs--Training. | Dogs--Behavior.

Classification: LCC SF427 .B4175 2022 | DDC 636.7/0887--dc23/eng/20220708

LC record available at https://lccn.loc.gov/2022026363

ISBN: 9781617813245   Printed in the U.S.A.

Table of Contents

Author's Note: Why a Workbook? v

How to Use This Workbook 1

Reminder: What Enrichment Is and Isn't 4

SPIDER Protocol 9

Protocol to Create an Enrichment Plan 11

The Enrichment Chart 12

Step 1: List Desirable and Undesirable Behaviors 15

Step 2: Are Needs Being Met? 20

Step 3: Are Agency Needs Being Met? 24

Step 4: Narrowing Down Potential Activities to Address Unmet Needs 28

Step 5: Prioritize Activities 32

Step 6: Develop a Plan of Action 34

Step 7: Implement and Document 37

Step 8: Reassess, Readdress, and Do It Again 40

Troubleshooting 41

Enrichment Protocol Case Study 47

Blank Charts 65

Desirable & Undesirable List... 66

"Are Needs Being Met?" Checklist... 67

Enrichment Chart 70

Agency Flowchart... 71

Author's Note: Why a Workbook?

When we wrote our book, *Canine Enrichment for the Real World,* we had originally wanted the subtitle to be: "What It Is, Why It Matters, and How to Incorporate It into Your Daily Life." We ultimately decided that it was too long for a subtitle, so we went in a different direction, but that original subtitle pretty much summed up our goal for the book: We wanted people to understand what enrichment really is, how it applies to them and their relationship with the animals they live and work with, and how to do it in an effective and sustainable way.

Even though we tried to provide as much applicability as possible, including our enrichment chart and a robust Resources section, we ultimately realized that creating a companion workbook was the best way to help people take the concepts we shared in the book and apply them to their own lives.

In the time since we wrote the book, we have had the opportunity to work with hundreds of clients and professionals around the world, focusing on using an enrichment framework to assess and address undesirable behaviors. We've gotten some great feedback, and these are some of the most common fears and concerns that people have shared with us:

From professionals:

- My client isn't interested in enrichment; they just want fast results.
- This seems too complicated for the average client to do.
- I'm not clear on how to apply this enrichment stuff in a training plan.

From pet parents:

- I feel guilty now that I know that some of my dog's needs aren't being met.
- If I let them do this behavior, aren't I reinforcing it? Isn't that a bad thing?
- I have a busy life and I'm not sure how I'll have time to do more for my dog. They already feel like so much work!

We will address all these fears and concerns in this workbook, we'll provide some worksheets that will help you to clarify and simplify your process, and we'll also provide a clear plan of action for implementing a sustainable and effective enrichment protocol for yourself or your clients.

So let's get started!

How to Use This Workbook

As dog professionals, our skills are constantly growing and evolving. Our knowledge of canine behavior and training techniques has evolved significantly in recent years. It is not surprising, therefore, that by the time *Canine Enrichment for the Real World* was published, we had already started a list of things we wanted to change or amend if we ever got the chance for a second edition. One of the biggest ways we've evolved since the book came out is how we implement the strategies we outlined in it. We've had the pleasure of discussing enrichment with so many people (thank you, all!) via webinars, courses, podcasts, interviews, Facebook groups, emails, and working with clients and students. The theme that we found folks coming back to is, "How can I implement this?"

Learning how to answer that question was an entire journey for us in and of itself. Sometimes you've been doing something for so long that it becomes second nature; you can't really explain how it is that you do what you do. You just do it.

Shortly after *Canine Enrichment for the Real World* (referred to hereafter as *CEftRW*) came out, we found ourselves having to analyze our strategies and compile them in a way that other people could replicate it. Especially since, while we originally wrote *CEftRW* for professionals, we've found many pet parents coming to us having read our book (shout out to all the awesome pet parents out there!). Whatever strategies we came up with, we knew they had to be replicable by people with a wide array of skill levels. We continued honing the process until we had a protocol and resources that other people were finding helpful.

And once the process and resources were in place, a workbook just made sense. Around the same time, our company Pet Harmony, an animal behavior and training organization that provides behavior consulting services for dogs, cats, and other species, began teaching these processes to behavioral professionals around the world. Thus, the Pet Harmony Enrichment Framework was born.

This workbook is to show you the process that we go through when creating an enrichment plan and provide you with resources to help you develop and/or grow those skills.

How this workbook is organized
This workbook is divided into four parts:

1. Basic enrichment overview

2. Explanation and examples of the enrichment process

3. Case study

4. Blank worksheets for you to use

The basic enrichment overview is to provide you with a quick review of what we discussed in the book, with one new section about behavioral diversity.

The explanation and examples of the enrichment process is the how-to for implementation. This is the nuts and bolts of how we do what we do.

The case study looks at one of Allie's clients. In it, she goes through the entire enrichment process so you can see it all laid out in detail. This case study is primarily for professionals, since it demonstrates how we use the enrichment framework to address maladaptive behaviors. But of course, pet parents, you're welcome to read it too, if you're interested!

Finally, the fourth section contains blank worksheets that we showcase throughout the implementation section. You can use them for your own dog or with a client's dog, if you so desire. For PDF versions of these worksheets, you can go to petharmonytraining.com/enrichmentworksheets.

More what we'd call 'guidelines' than actual rules

Just because we do something a certain way does not mean it's the only way to do it. Consider this workbook more as a guideline, rather than the One True Way. Furthermore, while we've developed many resources to help folks go through the process, we rarely use them ourselves. We typically go through the process outlined in this workbook in our heads or will shorten it when possible. At the end of the day, you have agency to go through this process in whatever way is effective for you. We strongly recommend starting with the "Are needs being met?" worksheet, since that is by far the tool we give most often to clients.

That said, there are times when we will use these resources, and it's usually when we're either working with someone who wants to see the entire process or when we're stuck. There are times in a case where some things are just not quite adding up, and when that happens it can be incredibly helpful to go back to the basics to see what we're missing and work through the case methodically and meticulously.

If it ain't that broke, it doesn't need much fixing

Since we do have more pet parents here than we expected (hello!), we think it's necessary to say that if your dog doesn't have any behavior issues that are causing disharmony in your home, your process will likely be much simpler than what we've outlined in this workbook. We as behavior consultants routinely apply this protocol to pets with serious maladaptive behaviors and wanted to showcase how enrichment isn't just for making twerpy adolescents less annoying or for keeping adult dogs entertained; it can (and should!) be used for serious behavior cases. However, we recognize that that does not apply to everyone who will be reading this, and not everyone will need to go as in depth for their individual dog. Again: We strongly recommend that you just start with the "Are needs being met?" checklist, since that may be all you need to identify and create goals for yourself.

If it is pretty broke, professional help is necessary

That said, if you are a pet parent who does have a dog with behavior problems, going through this workbook unguided is not recommended. A qualified behavior professional will be able to give you invaluable information and help when it comes to safely and effectively implementing the enrichment strategies we've laid out here. We routinely have to alter exercises for pets with maladaptive behaviors in order to keep them and others safe and to make those exercises effective. We do not expect the average pet parent to be able to do that.

Enrichment plans are cyclical

You will never be done with an enrichment plan. It's not something to finish or something that has a final destination. Needs evolve as we and our environment change. What your dog needs at 6 months old is not the same as what they need at 3 years old or 9 years old. We can't hang our hat on what used to work for them. We need to look at the individual who is here in front of us at this very moment. And that means adjusting our enrichment plan as their needs change. The good news is this means *you shouldn't feel guilty that your pet has unmet needs*. It's simply a part of life. If your dog is running around in the yard and playing, they'll become thirsty. That thirst is an unmet need. But that doesn't mean you're neglecting or abusing your dog, or that you have failed as a dog owner. It's just a normal, healthy need that has arisen, and it's simply a signal to you to provide fresh water to your dog. Think of all of enrichment like that: Unmet needs aren't a sign of failure on our part; they're just a function of being alive.

The Pet Harmony Enrichment Framework

Pet parents, this section is geared more toward professionals, so feel free to skip to the next section. As we've had the opportunity to speak more about enrichment with our colleagues, we've homed in on different aspects of enrichment that we and others refer to. A lot of these conversations have revolved around what is training versus behavior modification versus enrichment, and how they are connected. We'll explore some of those discussions in the next section.

But, more salient at the moment is that we've recognized that a larger discussion needs to happen about how enrichment in general should be applied to work with pet animals. We mentioned in Chapter 1 of *CEftRW* that enrichment often gets paired with training as if they were two pieces of a whole: enrichment-and-training. And while we mentioned that that's not necessarily the case, we never really discussed how the two interact with one another.

Because of that, we got questions along the lines of "How does this enrichment plan work with a behavior modification plan?" For those of you who've listened to some of our earlier interviews, you may have noticed us stumble over answering that question. It's taken a while for us to be able to better articulate it.

Enrichment is the framework in which all else resides: management, training, and the health and well-being protocols, including the ones we detail in the rest of this workbook. They're all parts of the Pet Harmony Enrichment Framework. At the end of the day, they're all tools to help us meet our animal's needs and should be viewed through the lens of enrichment, not vice versa.

How to do that is way beyond the scope of a workbook. If you're interested in using the Pet Harmony Enrichment Framework, we cover how to do this in our Enrichment Master Class available for professionals on our website: petharmonytraining.com/enrichmentframework.

Reminder: What Enrichment Is and Isn't

Before we launch into the rest of this workbook, it will be helpful to quickly recap what enrichment is and is not. We don't want you to have to reread the whole book, so we'll just hit the highlights here.

Let's start at the end and work backward from there. The goal of enrichment is for the animals in our care to be physically, behaviorally, and emotionally healthy so that they can express their natural (called "species-typical") behaviors.

For our animals to be physically, behaviorally, and emotionally healthy — and therefore in order for them to be able to express species-typical behaviors — we have to meet their needs.

In order to meet their needs, we need to be able to understand what their needs are, and then identify what needs of theirs are already being met, and which ones are not currently being met. And then we have to meet the unmet needs.

But that's not the end of it!

We then must observe whether or not our attempts at meeting their unmet needs were effective. One of the criteria we use to determine how well we've met those needs is that we're seeing observable behavior change in the direction we're wanting it to go.

Another criterion we use to determine whether their needs have been met is observing whether or not they are choosing to engage with the resources we have provided. The ability to make choices and have some measure of control over our outcomes is called **agency**.

If our attempts weren't successful — if the animal didn't choose to engage and/or behaviors aren't changing in the direction we want — we need to reassess, readdress, and try again.

So now that we've talked about what enrichment is, let's talk a little about what it isn't.

Toys and games aren't enrichment. Objects and activities certainly have the *potential* to be enriching, but they are not in and of themselves enrichment. The only way to determine whether any of those things is enriching is if we were using them to meet a specific need, and then we observe that the animal chooses to engage with them *and* the act of engaging with them achieves our intended goal. In other words, enrichment isn't the thing itself, but the contingent relationship between the thing and the outcome.

Training isn't enrichment. Like objects and activities, training absolutely has the *potential* to be enriching, but again, we can only determine if training is in fact enrichment by first assessing whether the learner chooses to engage, and second assessing whether training achieved our intended goal. Did that training effort result in an animal that is more physically, behaviorally, and emotionally healthy than they were before? Do they, as a result of that training, now have the opportunity and ability to perform species-typical behaviors in healthy, safe, and appropriate ways? If the answer is no, then that particular training wasn't enrichment.

Enrichment isn't just a synonym for reinforcement. There has been some confusion within the animal training community as to whether or not enrichment is just reinforcement. We understand why this confusion exists. Since both concepts involve behavior change, there is certainly a lot of overlap between the two concepts (they are both defined as contingencies, for example), and a lot of reinforcement does happen in enrichment. However, they are not necessarily interchangeable.

Reinforcement can be defined as the contingent relationship between a behavior and the following consequence, wherein that consequence increases the future probability of that behavior (it's a little more complicated than that, but for our purposes we'll go with this as the definition). Reinforcement is defined by that specific contingency: behavior happens → consequence happens → behavior is more likely to happen in the future when that consequence is likely to follow.

During enrichment, we are setting the stage for a wide variety of behaviors to occur, and as the result of a variety of factors. For example:

Let's say we give a dog a Kong with the goal of providing foraging and mental stimulation. The behavior changes we're hoping to see as a result of playing with the Kong include:

- Reduced counter-surfing replaced by more appropriate foraging behaviors
- Reduced destruction of property replaced by engagement with dog toys
- Reduced pacing and vocalization replaced by increased rest

If the dog interacts with the Kong, that isn't just one behavior. There are a whole variety of behaviors that a dog might perform to interact with the Kong — some of which are classically conditioned, some of which are unlearned species-typical behaviors (such as the foraging behaviors those toys are designed to elicit!), and of course, some of which are reinforced. Enrichment encompasses all those behaviors, not just one procedure or process. In other words, it doesn't matter whether the dog paws at the Kong, pushes it with their nose, picks it up in their mouth, knocks the food out to access it, or holds it in their paws to access the food by licking and chewing. Any of those behaviors would be acceptable; all that matters is that the dog engages with the Kong, and the outcome of that engagement is any or all the behavior changes described above.

With enrichment, we also hope to see the reduction of maladaptive behaviors, as described above, but no one would ever make the claim that enrichment is synonymous with punishment. The same is true for reinforcement.

And for that matter, not all reinforcement is enrichment! If you called your dog into the kitchen, and when they came into the kitchen you gave them an entire half gallon of ice cream, and that scenario happened every day, that would certainly be reinforcement but would certainly not be enrichment!

In summary:
- In the Venn diagram of enrichment and reinforcement, there's a lot of overlap between those two circles, but they aren't the same circle.
- Not all behavior is operant (i.e., the action → consequence contingency doesn't always exist).
- Not all enrichment is reinforcement.
- Not all reinforcement is enrichment.

Enrichment is not about entertainment. Of course, the byproduct of a lot of enrichment is that the animal is entertained, but that isn't always the case, nor is it necessarily the goal. Play is entertaining (when it's actually play, and not social interaction forced at gunpoint and then called "play"), but we wouldn't describe periods of rest as entertaining, and yet rest — and more specifically, learning how to rest as a way to self-regulate after a stressful situation — is an important component of health and well-being!

Enrichment is descriptive, not prescriptive. As we discussed several times above and in *CEftRW,* enrichment is defined by its outcomes, not our intentions.

Enrichment is **descriptive**. In other words, we first define our goals, then devise a plan to meet those goals, then we implement the plan, but we can only say that it was enrichment by observing whether or not the goals have been met.

A **prescriptive** approach would be, for example, buying some foraging toys because that's what the internet told you to do, setting them out for your dog, and then assuming that the toys are enrichment without either having a goal for those toys or observing whether or not the toys achieved the goal.

We always want to keep our eyes on the prize: Everything we do should be in service of physical, behavioral, and emotional health so that our pets are empowered to perform species-typical behaviors in safe, healthy, and appropriate ways.

Categories of enrichment

Enrichment can be broadly broken down into 14 categories:

- **Health/veterinary care**
- **Hygiene**
- **Nutrition**
- **Physical exercise**
- **Sensory stimulation**
- **Safety**
- **Security**
- **Species-typical behaviors** (Note: in *CeftRW* we called these "instinctual behaviors" because we were worried about not being accessible enough to pet parents, but we instantly regretted that decision. We will refer to them as "species-typical" for the remainder of the workbook.)
- **Foraging**
- **Social interactions**
- **Mental stimulation**
- **Calming**
- **Independence**
- **Environment**

There are seemingly endless possibilities for how you can meet these needs, but below are a few of the most common activities that we use to address each category.

Health and veterinary care
- Cooperative care training
- Regular vet visits
- Working with a veterinary behaviorist to get on a safe and effective medication protocol

Hygiene
- Cooperative care training

Nutrition

- Find a diet that your pet thrives on based on objective metrics such as blood work, body condition score, coat quality, reducing/eliminating inflammation, GI health, and behavior

Physical exercise

- Walks

- Flirt pole

- Games like tug, fetch, and hide and seek

- Swimming

- Dog sports

- Playing with other dogs

Sensory stimulation

- Scent games like scent tubes, scatter feeding games such as "Find It" or "Go Hunt," or K9 Nosework

- Sniffaris

- Adventure walks/adventure boxes

- Massage, T-Touch, Jin Shin Jyutsu, etc.

- Texture, food, or toy preference tests

- Visual masking via Calming Caps, window film, or other tools to reduce visual overstimulation

- Sound masking options to drown out stressful sounds outside

Safety

- Leash, harness, and/or recall training

- Basket muzzle training

- Secure yard

- Removing poisonous plants from your yard and home

Security

- Limiting or eliminating exposure to stressors until the dog has the skills to navigate those stressors

- Creating a safe space for your dog

- Teaching your dog to move away from stressors

Species-typical behaviors

- Tug

- Flirt pole

- Fetch

- Digging pits

- K9 Nosework, scatter feeding, sniffaris, snuffle mats

- Food puzzles

- Dog sports

- Chew toys

Foraging

- K9 Nosework, scatter feeding, sniffaris, snuffle mats

- Food puzzles

Social interaction
- Snuggle time with your dog!
- Play and outings with your dog
- Doggie dates for dogs who enjoy one or two friends
- Playgroups, dog daycares, or dog parks for dogs who are social butterflies

Mental stimulation
- Some kinds of training
- Food puzzles at the appropriate difficulty level
- Some dog sports

Calming
- Relaxation protocols that create conditions for a dog to relax on their own and put it on cue rather than trying to force relaxation by controlling body position
- Designated rest periods
- An environment that facilitates rest
- Scents and sounds that are effective at masking stressors and can be classically conditioned to elicit relaxation

Independence
- Providing choices and teaching your dog how to make choices on their own
- Teaching your dog how to be comfortable being alone

Environment
- Creating a space that reduces stressors, provides opportunities for rest, exploration, and play, and enables the dog to move freely between spaces and either solicit or retreat from social interaction as desired

Behavioral diversity

There is a concept in animal welfare called behavioral diversity. Behavioral diversity refers to the rich variety of behaviors that wild animals have the freedom to perform each day. It is our responsibility as caregivers of domesticated and captive-bred animals to provide them with that same variety — if not always the exact same repertoire — of species-typical behaviors that their wild and feral counterparts enjoy. It is a key component of our enrichment strategies.

Oftentimes, when we're just focused on trying to make an annoying behavior stop, the training and management approaches can be really restrictive for the animal. They place a heavy emphasis on "correcting" — or shutting down — the behavior, and then restricting the animal's options. A lot of these training philosophies involve crating dogs for as much as 20 hours a day. These methods are popular because they appear to work quickly and it can be convenient for the owner, who can just forget about their dog for most of the day and only bring them out of the crate for a few hours for specific activities, like feeding or walking.

One of the biggest problems with these training methods is that animals aren't little robots that you can just turn off and put on a shelf until you feel like pulling them back out again. Animals are sentient beings with complex emotional and behavioral needs. Restricting movement might be convenient and provide the owner with a sense of relief and control, but it isn't addressing the *reasons* for the maladaptive behavior(s), nor is it acknowledging and meeting the animal's needs.

The belief that *either* animals are allowed freedoms and will wreak havoc *or* they must be controlled and contained for all or most of their lives is a false dichotomy. It is both possible and necessary to learn how to provide them with ample freedom to enjoy behavioral diversity *and* teach them how to live and operate safely at home and elsewhere. We can meet the needs of both the pet and the owner and improve their relationship with each other by doing so.

SPIDER Protocol

SPIDER is a framework that was created for zoos, aviaries, and aquariums to objectively create and assess their enrichment programs. We briefly referenced it in *CeftRW*, but didn't really go into much detail about it, so let's discuss its relevance to this workbook. But first, we acknowledge that anti-zoo sentiments have become quite strong in the past years among pet parents, pet industries, and animal rights groups. This is ironic for a couple of reasons:

1. Zoos, aviaries, and aquariums that are accredited by zoological welfare organizations such as the AZA, ZAA, or EAZA employ staff who are educated about animal welfare and enrichment, and whose jobs are to create and implement extensive enrichment plans that far surpass those of almost any shelter, rescue group, sanctuary, training facility, or dog daycare facility.

2. The very concepts of animal welfare and enrichment, which pet industries started becoming aware of in the past couple of decades or so and have tried to emulate, *came from zoos.* In other words, the pet community borrowed concepts from the zoo community and then used those concepts to turn around and attack the community they borrowed from.

Since education is the best way to combat polarization and hostility among groups with common goals, let's learn a little bit about SPIDER, which stands for:

Setting goals, which includes:

- Learning the natural and individual history of the animals you work with
- Clearly identifying desirable and undesirable behaviors you hope to change through enrichment
- Taking into account the activity budget for the species as a whole and the individual(s) you're working with

Planning, which includes:

- Creating an enrichment plan that provides the individual(s) with agency
- Deciding which behaviors to encourage and which ones to prevent through careful management
- Considering safety, practicality, and logistical implementation
- Establishing an approval process among everyone who will be implementing the plan and the professionals who are overseeing the whole process

Implementation, which includes:

- Carrying out the enrichment plan
- Creating an enrichment calendar to track what happens when
- Scheduling variation and novelty to maintain engagement without compromising predictability and increasing stress

Documentation, which includes:

- Noting in the enrichment calendar what happened when
- Recording videos and taking photos
- Keeping written logs of noteworthy events, interactions, responses, and outcomes
- Using computerized tracking programs to track and measure outcomes

Evaluation, which includes:

- Reviewing documentation to determine effectiveness
- Deciding what, if anything, needs to be changed and how to change it

Readjustment, which includes:

- Going through the process again with the decided upon changes

If you're either a behavior professional or a pet parent who has worked with a behavior professional, some of these steps might sound very familiar to you, and very similar to what you already do to address maladaptive behaviors. Some of it, on the other hand, might be completely new to you, and sound like a whole lot of extra and unnecessary work, or like it doesn't really apply to dogs living in pet homes.

And if you're a pet parent whose dog is mostly fine, and you're just here because you want to make your dog's life the best it can be, this all might seem like waaaaaaaay overkill. And you'd be right!

As much as we honor the SPIDER framework and unabashedly borrow heavily from it, we realized we needed to make a framework that was more applicable to dog owners and trainers, and create resources that could get the general point across for people who just want to improve their dogs' lives.

Protocol to Create an Enrichment Plan

As we said in the previous section, the SPIDER framework is fantastic and an incredibly useful tool for zoos, but we needed to make a parallel framework that better meets the needs of pet owners and pet professionals. So we made the following tweaks in our enrichment protocol:

- Omitted the parts that are irrelevant to pet owners and trainers
- Simplified the parts that are necessary for addressing maladaptive behaviors but don't need to be quite as rigorous in a pet home (helloooo simpler data collection!)
- Split the parts that are unavoidably complex into smaller, simpler steps to make them easier for pet parents and professionals to implement
- Created resources — such as the "Are needs being met?" checklist — that work just fine as standalone worksheets for pet owners who don't need to address any maladaptive behaviors but are simply looking for ways to improve their dogs' lives

Here's the protocol we developed for systematically creating an enrichment plan:

1. List desirable and undesirable behaviors
2. Are needs being met?
3. Are agency needs being met?
4. Narrow down your options
5. Prioritize activities
6. Develop plan of action
7. Implement
8. Reassess, readdress, and do it again

The rest of this workbook will be devoted to breaking down and expanding upon each step.

Use your observational skills
This protocol relies heavily on reading canine body language and observing overt behaviors. These are skills that can be learned and fine-tuned, just like any other. If you are not proficient in these skills yet, we recommend focusing on them before or as you go through your enrichment process.

The Enrichment Chart

In *CeftRW* we shared with you an enrichment chart that helps put the majority of that protocol onto one page.

Pet Harmony Enrichment Chart

Aspect of Enrichment	Is This Need Being Met?	Is There Agency?	Priority	Plan of Action
Health/Veterinary				
Hygiene				
Diet/Nutrition				
Physical Exercise				
Sensory Stimulation				
Safety				
Security				
Instinctual Behaviors				
Foraging				
Social Interaction				
Mental Exercise				
Independence				
Environment				
Calming				

As we go through each step of the enrichment protocol, we'll refer back to what that looks like on the enrichment chart. But first, a few notes about the enrichment chart.

It's a tool, not a necessity

The enrichment chart is merely a tool to help you collect and organize your thoughts succinctly. But it's just that: a tool. It's not a necessity for going through the Pet Harmony Enrichment Framework. Truthfully, even though it's a tool we created, we rarely actually complete an enrichment chart when we work with clients. We go through the steps in our head and present the information in a much simpler (read: less overwhelming) way to our clients.

The only times we use it is when either the client specifically asks to use the enrichment chart, or we're stuck on something in the case, and we want to do a full inventory of unmet needs to try to suss out the missing pieces of the puzzle.

If you find using the chart superfluous, then don't use it. If you find it helpful, then do use it. Do whatever helps you the most.

Recommended nomenclature

In the process of filling out the chart for clients and presentations, we started refining the process. With that came nomenclature that simultaneously makes sense to us when we are filling out charts and puts a focus on not alienating or shaming our clients. This lets us fill out enrichment charts more quickly and accurately, especially when we have multiple consultants working on the same case. Below is what we've come up with:

Are needs being met?
- Likely (L or checkmark): "I believe this need is being met!"

- In progress (IP): "I'm already actively working on this."

- Potential room for growth (PRFG): "We may need to address this."

- Room for growth (RFG): "We definitely need to address this."

> **Why "likely" and not "yes"?**
> Using the word "likely" is more accurate than using the word "yes" in this context. It's virtually impossible for us to know with 100% certainty that another individual's needs are being met. We have metrics, absolutely, but the metrics that we have are not the be-all-end-all. We opted for "likely" to remind folks that we can't just cross something off the list forever; there's a possibility that we'll need to address that category in the future.

Are agency needs being met?
- Appropriate (A): "My dog has agency and it's appropriate to provide that in this context."

- In progress (IP): "I'm already actively working on this."

- Potential room for growth (PRFG): "We may need to address this."

- Room for growth (RFG): "We definitely need to address this."

- Inappropriate (IA): "My dog has agency and it's inappropriate to provide that in this context."

Prioritization

When working with clients, it's important to break up the enrichment plan into sustainable steps. For this reason, we talk to our clients about their behavior change journey in terms of phases. After we've figured out what needs we want to meet and how we're going to meet them, we break them up into phases. For example, "In Phase 1, we'll work on scent work and the relaxation protocol. In Phase 2, we'll start working on the Flight cue. In Phase 3, we'll add in Look at That."

So, our first prioritization in the example given above is scent work and the relaxation protocol, but we may need to try a few different scent work strategies to find the one that works best for that individual dog and their family. Let's say that the first thing we want to try is scatter feeding, but if that isn't the best strategy for this particular client, we'll try a snuffle mat next. Our nomenclature for that process looks like this:

- 1.1: First try at the first prioritization strategy (in the example above, scatter feeding and the relaxation protocol)

- 1.2: Second try at the first prioritization strategy (in the example above, a snuffle mat)

- 2.1: First try at the second prioritization strategy (in the example above, the Flight Cue)

Do what works for you

As you're filling out your enrichment chart, give this nomenclature a try to see how you like it. But at the end of the day, you have agency, and you're welcome to fill out the chart in any way that makes sense to you.

Step 1: List Desirable and Undesirable Behaviors

Step 1 of the enrichment protocol is pretty straightforward: list desirable and undesirable behaviors. The purpose of this step is simple. You can't know how successful your plan is if you don't know what your goals are.

Remember back to Part 1 in which we talked about taking a descriptive instead of a prescriptive approach to enrichment. A descriptive approach means observing the effects that our enrichment plan has on an animal's behavior. We need to know what behaviors we want to increase and decrease in order to make those observations meaningful, so that's where a list of desirable and undesirable behaviors comes into play.

We recommend listing current desirable and undesirable behaviors and goal behaviors. A worksheet that you can use for this step can be found in the blank worksheets section at the end of this workbook.

Here is an example of this step:

Boo Boo is a 7-year-old medium-large mixed breed. She has had several incidents of attacking neighborhood dogs both on leash and when she escapes from the house. Here is an example of how her chart might look:

Current/existing desirable behaviors:	Current/existing undesirable behaviors:
• Plays with resident dog • Plays with and performs other affiliative behaviors with human household-members • Responds to training cues • Relaxed behaviors seen when no triggers present	• Lunges, barks, growls on leash when sees another dog • Pushes past family members and runs through open doors • Bit resident dog when she walked near her bone • Displays fearful body language during thunderstorms and other loud noises • Stiff and sometimes will lunge at strangers • Barks at doorbell • Barks when seeing dogs through the window • Chases the cat
Goal behaviors: • Be able to calmly walk past another dog on walks • Remain in the house when the door to the garage is open • Remain on one side of a baby gate • Go to her crate when the doorbell rings	

We'll get to a few more examples of this, but first, two notes to consider when completing this step.

Overt, not covert behaviors

When you're listing desirable and undesirable behaviors, it's important to stick to **overt behaviors**. Overt behaviors are behaviors that we can observe and measure. Examples of overt behaviors include:

- The dog sniffed the food puzzle, then walked away.
- The cat's ears are pinned flat against her head.
- The horse took three steps to the left.
- The parrot stepped up onto the finger.

There's no debate as to whether these behaviors happened or didn't happen; we can clearly observe and measure them.

Compare that to internal thoughts, feelings, motivations, and intentions, or **covert behaviors**. Assumptions that we make about covert behaviors are called **constructs**. Here are examples of some constructs:

- The dog is jumping on the person because he hasn't learned manners.
- The dog is jumping on the person because he's trying to dominate them.
- The dog is jumping on the person because he's excited to see them.
- The dog is jumping on the person because he's anxious and telling them to go away.

Here we have the same overt behavior — jumping on the person — but four different interpretations, or constructs, as to the internal thoughts, feelings, motivations, and intentions that are fueling that behavior.

We will never know if our constructs are correct. Take a moment to reread that sentence and let it sink in. It's impossible for us to know if our constructs are correct; they are educated guesses at best and likely hopelessly wrong the majority of the time.

Below is an example of how we can turn constructs into overt behaviors when filling out this worksheet.

Constructs of covert behaviors	Overt behaviors
Current/existing desirable behaviors: • Friendly with humans in house • Likes resident dog • Likes learning	Current/existing desirable behaviors: • Plays and snuggles with humans in house • Plays and snuggles with resident dog • Approaches trainer with a loose and wiggly body
Current/existing undesirable behaviors: • Bosses the other dog around • Goes after the cat • Does not like other dogs	Current/existing undesirable behaviors: • Inserts herself between the resident dog and owners when resident dog is being petted • Chases the cat when the cat starts walking • Barks, lunges, growls, and bites other dogs
Goal behaviors: • Fine being around other dogs • Owners are able to trust her behavior around other dogs	Goal behaviors: • Calmly walks past other dogs, including being able to look at and look away from them • Dog can rest and play in the presence of other dogs

See how much clearer the overt behaviors are compared to the constructs?

Constructs aren't necessarily a bad thing; we use them all the time! They're an easy shorthand when everyone involved is using the same operational definition. If instead of saying a dog has "leash reactivity" we had to say a dog "barks, lunges, and growls when they see other dogs while on a leash" we'd never get anything done! Constructs make for convenient shortcuts in conversations, but because they are only assumptions, we cannot make behavior decisions based on them. We can and should only make behavior and enrichment decisions based on overt behaviors.

Another type of verbiage that comes out alongside constructs are **labels**. Labels are words we use to describe who someone intrinsically is, their personality, or their character. Examples of labels include:

• Dominant
• Sweet
• Aggressive
• Friendly
• Bomb-proof

Again, a problem with labels is that they're assumptions at best and detrimental at worst. The same dog may be labeled as "fearful" or "aggressive" after a bite, and the outcomes for that dog are often dependent on the words we choose to use to label them and their behavior. Labels have a way of creeping into our list of desirable and undesirable behaviors; we shouldn't let them.

Labels	Overt behaviors
Current/existing desirable behaviors: • Sweet with people she knows • Friendly with dogs she knows	Current/existing desirable behaviors: • Plays and snuggles with humans in house • Plays and snuggles with resident dog
Current/existing undesirable behaviors: • Dominant with dogs • Mean to cats	Current/existing undesirable behaviors: • Inserts herself between the resident dog and owners when resident dog is being petted • Chases the cat when the cat starts walking
Goal behaviors: • Fine being around other dogs	Goal behaviors: • Calmly walk past other dogs, including being able to look at and look away from them

Again, labels can be convenient tools for conversation when we're defining them the same way. But, from our experience, definitions differ drastically depending on the person! We have so many clients who come to us after their dog or puppy starts displaying anxiety-related behaviors after coming home. When we ask them what they were like when they picked up their new companion, we often hear, "They were so calm! Much calmer than everyone else around them." The conversation usually turns to a discussion about shut down behavior and/or learned helplessness, and that what they were calling "calm" we would have labeled "anxious." We need to define a label for it to be an effective communication tool.

Does it pass the Dead Man Test?

The Dead Man Test was created by Ogden Lindsley in 1965 as a general rule to determine whether something is or is not a behavior. As Malott and Saurez say in the 2003 version of *Principles of Behavior,* "If a dead man can do it, it ain't behavior, and if a dead man can't do it, then it is behavior."

So often we focus on what we *don't* want our dogs to do:

- Stop jumping
- Don't bark at dogs passing by
- Stop biting people
- Don't get into the trash

The problem with this is that the above statements don't pass the Dead Man Test. A dead man cannot-jump, not-bark-at-dogs-passing-by, not-bite-people, or not-get-into-the-trash. Those statements don't describe a behavior, they describe the lack thereof. And we can't train or teach a non-behavior. We can only teach behaviors.

Instead of focusing on what we *don't* want our dogs to do, we need to focus on what we want them to do:

- Sit when greeting people
- Calmly and quietly watch dogs passing by
- Move away from people when they're uncomfortable
- Forage using food puzzles

We need to apply the Dead Man Test to our list of desirable and undesirable behaviors, too.

Doesn't Pass the Dead Man Test	Passes the Dead Man Test
Current/existing desirable behaviors: • Doesn't fight with the resident dog • Doesn't have problems with humans in household	Current/existing desirable behaviors: • Plays and snuggles with humans in house • Plays and snuggles with resident dog
Current/existing undesirable behaviors: • Doesn't do well when other dog is getting petted	Current/existing undesirable behaviors: • Inserts herself between the resident dog and owners when resident dog is being petted
Goal behaviors: • Stop attacking other dogs	Goal behaviors: • Calmly walk past other dogs, including being able to look at and look away from them

Remembering the Dead Man Test allows us to create a crystal clear understanding of what we want the dog to do so we can elicit those behaviors through our enrichment plan — either by teaching them how to do them, creating conditions that allow the desirable species-typical behaviors to naturally occur in the desired context, or creating associations between the desired behaviors and things the dog really loves, so the dog learns to love the desired behaviors, too.

Step 2: Are Needs Being Met?

Now that we know what our goals are, we need to know where we're starting from. We already have some of that information from the current desirable and undesirable behavior categories from Step 1, but now we need to get more specific as far as what the root problems are. We need to determine which of the enrichment categories have room for improvement.

By and large, one of the most common questions we got after *CEftRW* came out was how to do this. Below is a checklist we've created to help you look at how well needs are being met overall in each enrichment category:

Health/Veterinary

- ✓ Regular vet visits
- ✓ Up to date on vaccinations or the equivalent
- ✓ Pain management if needed
- ✓ Management for physical and mental health concerns: medication, physical therapy, surgery, etc.

Hygiene (remember that this is dependent on breed/morphology)

- ✓ Appropriate amount of bathing
- ✓ Appropriate skin and coat care
- ✓ Ear cleaning
- ✓ Nail trims
- ✓ Dental hygiene
- ✓ Other breed-specific hygiene practices

Diet/Nutrition

- ✓ Appropriate diet for the individual, no health concerns
- ✓ Treats for different scenarios

Physical Exercise

- ✓ Amount of physical activity appreciably reduces fidgeting and other boredom-based behaviors
- ✓ Type of exercise does not compromise physical or mental health (e.g., exacerbates joint disease, causes distress, etc.)

Sensory Stimulation

- ✓ Absence of stereotypical behaviors
- ✓ Opportunities for behavioral diversity
- ✓ The environment does not elicit stress responses the majority of the time

Safety

- ✓ Does not have access to poisonous foods, medications, plants, household items
- ✓ Is not able to interact with animals who would cause bodily or psychological harm, including domestic species, predators, and wildlife
- ✓ Is not able to run into the street or other harmful environments
- ✓ Is not able to interact with humans who would cause bodily or psychological harm
- ✓ Is not exposed to harmful husbandry or training methods and tools

Security

- ✓ Has at least one space in their environment to retreat to where they are exposed to minimal stressors
- ✓ Knows how to move away from stressors when necessary
- ✓ Knows how to investigate novel stimuli
- ✓ Displays fear- or avoidance-related behaviors only in response to reasonable, novel, and/or extraordinary stimuli

Instinctual Behaviors (including but not limited to: chewing, shredding, digging, barking, chasing, investigating, scavenging, etc.)

- ✓ Has opportunities to display species- or breed-typical behaviors in healthy, safe, and appropriate ways
- ✓ Appropriate species- or breed-typical behaviors are performed with enough frequency and diversity so as to reduce nuisance behaviors

Foraging

- ✓ Knows how to track and/or trail scents
- ✓ Knows how to problem-solve in manipulating objects to obtain food
- ✓ The majority of their caloric intake is consumed via foraging
- ✓ Has daily opportunities to perform above behaviors

Social Interaction

- ✓ Is able to interact with individuals (relative to their level of sociability) in healthy, safe, and appropriate ways
- ✓ Is not forced to interact with distressing individuals and/or species
- ✓ Is able to display a diversity of behaviors in the presence of others
- ✓ Displays appropriate play solicitation behaviors, including breaks and self-regulation

Mental Exercise

- ✓ Regular opportunities to learn new or expand on existing skills
- ✓ Regular opportunities to track and/or trail scents
- ✓ Regular opportunities to problem-solve

Independence

- ✓ Is able to self-entertain
- ✓ Displays no or minimal distress signals when left alone
- ✓ Is able to problem-solve situations with minimal human guidance
- ✓ Is able to appropriately communicate needs

Environment

- ✓ Is provided with predictability, including a predictable schedule/routines, predictable outcomes, and a reasonably predictable environment (the level of predictability necessary is relative to the individual, based on overall behavioral health)
- ✓ Regular access to basic necessities
- ✓ Regular access to opportunities for species-typical behaviors and behavioral diversity
- ✓ Minimal exposure to chronic or acute stressors

Calming

- ✓ Takes midday naps
- ✓ Sleeps soundly at night
- ✓ Is able to relax in well-known environments
- ✓ Is able to self-soothe and self-regulate

While this checklist may show you that there are categories that have room for improvement, that doesn't mean that all those categories are relevant to the goals of the enrichment plan. For example, you may determine that a dog's hygiene needs could be better met, but that has nothing to do with the leash reactivity they're displaying. This checklist will show you the broad picture, but the behaviors listed in Step 1 will help you determine what is currently relevant. Everything can be revisited after primary issues are addressed.

There are a couple of ways to think about your Step 1 behaviors and how they relate to a category of enrichment:

1. What need is the undesirable behavior meeting?
2. What category (or categories) would be impacted by an increase in the desirable behaviors?

What need is the undesirable behavior meeting?

Our go-to example of this is counter-surfing, which meets the need for foraging. Foraging is the act of searching for and finding food. Counter surfing (usually) is exactly that: searching for and finding food. It's simply being done in a way that most people find inappropriate and, depending on the type of food, unsafe.

In order to determine what needs the undesirable behavior may be meeting (because we can't always know for sure), we should look at what is driving the current behavior. Is it a modal action pattern? (As we discussed in *CEftRW*, MAPs are unlearned, innate, species-typical behaviors that serve a functional purpose.) Is it a classically conditioned behavior? Is it being reinforced? What do they get out of doing that behavior?

For example, counter-surfing requires searching for and sometimes problem-solving to acquire delicious food. What categories look similar to that behavior? Foraging, as mentioned, and perhaps mental stimulation if there's a good deal of problem-solving that goes into it (e.g., push the chair next to the table, jump from the chair onto the table, jump from the table onto the counter.)

Another example: A dog who is chasing the cat is exhibiting a modal action pattern. Since MAPs are species-typical behaviors, the category that is related to this particular behavior is the species-typical category.

To recap how to determine what need an undesirable behavior is meeting:

1. Observe what's driving the current behavior. (Pet parents: We don't expect you to be able to do this on your own! That's what behavior professionals are for!)
2. What are they getting out of it?
3. Look at the categories to determine which are affected.

When we're talking about needs, which needs are being met by undesirable behaviors, and which categories are affected, we really can't avoid wandering into covert behavior territory. We recognize this. That means we will not know for sure if we're correct until we start experimenting with our enrichment plan and observing the outcomes. It's okay to be unsure here. That's the whole reason we included a "Potential Room for Growth" option in the enrichment chart nomenclature for those moments when you're not sure where a particular behavior fits.

Which skills in which category or categories would increase desirable behaviors?

Looking at undesirable behaviors is only half of the equation. We also need to look at which skills would increase those desirable behaviors listed in Step 1. An example of this that we see frequently is dogs who are always on the go. Their parents are exercising and training them for hours a day and they still never seem to get tired. Learning how to relax would be a wonderful skill here! For a case like this, instead of looking at the mental and physical exercise categories, we might first look at the calming category and teach the dog how to relax.

Another example would be a dog who has poor play skills with other dogs, resulting in rushing up upon first meeting them and continuing to solicit play after the other dog has displayed distance-increasing signals. This dog may get quite a bit of social interaction, but it looks like they still have some skill-building to do within the social interaction category (and perhaps calming as well!).

There is obviously a lot of variation and complexity in addressing behavior issues, but in general, the majority of maladaptive behaviors benefit from help in the security, species-typical, environment, and calming categories, whereas nuisance behaviors tend to benefit from mental exercise, physical exercise, foraging, species-typical behaviors, and calming. That said, this is certainly not set in stone, so remember: Behavior is a study of one!

Step 3: Are Agency Needs Being Met?

Recall that agency is a necessary component of each category. Because of that, we gave this concept its own column in the enrichment chart. You may have noticed that it was conspicuously absent in the Step 2 checklist. That's because it's possible to meet the primary needs of a category without fulfilling the agency criterion, and vice versa. For example, many pets' needs are being met when it comes to the health/veterinary category, but few have agency within thatcategory. If we're to truly meet an individual's needs, we also need to provide agency in as many aspects of their lives as possible.

One of the biggest questions we've received with regard to agency (and just in general) is: How do I know if it's appropriate to give my dog agency in this category or situation? And how do I know if I'm giving my dog enough options or choices?

The answer to this question isn't cut and dried. It's dependent on the situation and the individuals involved. So instead of a checklist to help navigate this step, we've developed an agency flowchart:

Does Your Pet Have Agency?

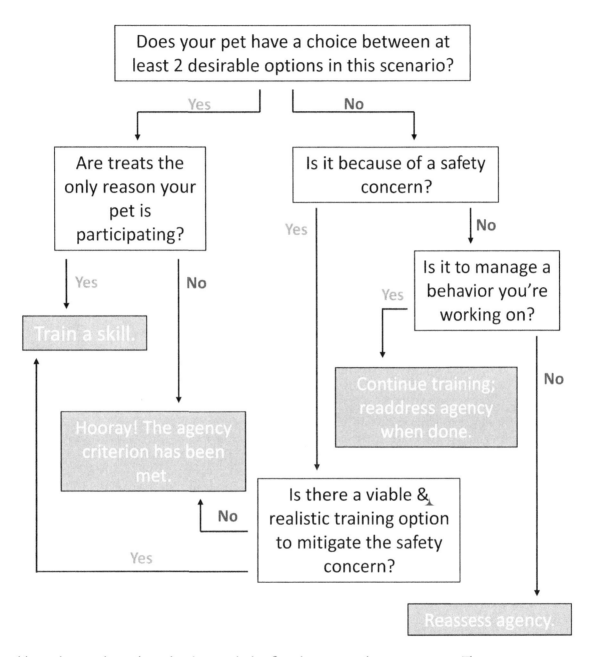

Just like with everything else we've discussed, this flowchart is a tool, not a necessity. There are some situations where it's pretty easy to see if the agency needs are being met. In those situations you likely will not need to use this tool.

Before we get into some examples using this flowchart, let's look at a few of the components.

Overall versus specific circumstances

There are two ways that you can use this flowchart: for overall agency within a category or for a specific circumstance. There is merit to either approach. When we're taking stock of overall well-being, or different circumstances are pretty similar within a category, we'll use the chart and consider overall agency. If there are situations that an animal is struggling with, we will often then narrow our focus to that one situation. Use this flowchart in whatever way is helpful to what you're currently working through.

A limited number of *desirable* options

Note that the flowchart starts with deciding if your pet has a choice between at least two desirable options. Agency isn't about unlimited options, and more is not necessarily better. In fact, being given unlimited options is often stressful, for both humans and non-humans! Anyone who has been to a restaurant with a 20-page menu, or who has been told by a professor that their next essay can be on any topic, can probably relate to this phenomenon. In order to meet the agency criterion, our pets can have as few as two desirable options.

However, those options do need to be actually desirable to your pet (not necessarily to you). An example of that is a pet who has a choice between getting rewarded for engaging in cooperative care and also getting rewarded for taking a break from it. It would not be considered having agency if they had a choice between engaging in cooperative care or getting pinned down if they try to say no to cooperative care. A "do it or else" situation doesn't fly; "tea and cake or death" isn't actually a choice.

Safety trumps agency

One of the most common reasons your pet will not have as many choices is due to safety concerns. Leashes are an example of this. It would be wonderful if our pets could be always off leash, but the reality is that being off leash presents a huge safety (and often legal) concern in the majority of circumstances for city dwellers. Do not allow your pet the opportunity to make a choice that could injure themselves or someone else until they have extensive training under their belt and are unlikely to cause injury anymore.

Agency needs are fluid

Just like enrichment, agency needs are fluid as well. We'll be able to readdress the choices that an animal has as they continue learning and gaining skills. We may need to limit choices for now that we'll be able to provide later.

Viable and realistic

You'll notice in the flowchart that we include "viable and realistic training options." Just because we *can* technically train something doesn't mean that we *should,* or that it's a viable option in certain situations. In addition to being desirable to the pet, the options need to be viable to everyone, i.e., realistic and sustainable for the humans and the pet. A choice between running loose in a securely fenced yard and going on a 10-mile hike may be great for the pet, but if the owner doesn't have the physical ability or time to go on the 10-mile hike, the second option does not pass the viability test. And could we technically teach a dog to share his food dish with the other dog in the house? Sure. Is anyone willing to go through the months and months of the labor-intensive and riskier option of behavior modification instead of simply feeding in a separate room? I've yet to meet that hypothetical person. When we're looking at training as a solution for allowing our pet more choices, we need to discard any options that aren't realistic for this particular household and situation.

Food can be used coercively

When we think of coercive training, we usually think about teaching via modeling, using aversive tools, or relying on pain, fear, and intimidation to train. However, food and treats can also be used coercively, and the results can be equally troublesome.

A common example we see is when people lure dogs closer to people whom they're uncomfortable with for food (i.e., making a dog with stranger danger take chicken from the stranger's hand). Just as with other coercive techniques, the outcome isn't always bad. Sometimes these dogs will learn that people aren't so bad. But other times they'll learn to approach strangers who make them uncomfortable, take the food from them, and then bite them. This is why we advocate so strongly for teaching pets to move away from individuals who make them uncomfortable. We've seen what can happen when a pet is forced or cajoled closer. Another common version of this is hand feeding for a dog displaying resource guarding behaviors around their food dish.

What this all means for agency is that if treats are the only reason your pet is participating in an activity or situation, then it doesn't technically meet the criteria as a desirable option. The activity in and of itself isn't desirable. There are, of course, situations where this isn't going to be true, like food puzzles. The whole point of those is to get food out of them. The situations where this is more salient include things like veterinary care, grooming, and social situations.

Step 4: Narrowing Down Potential Activities to Address Unmet Needs

Steps 1-3 of the enrichment protocol set us up to understand where the dog currently is: their baseline. Now that we have a thorough understanding of where we're starting and our end goal, we can focus on how we're going to get there. Step 4 starts us off with that by narrowing down the potential activities we can implement for the unmet needs we've identified.

As you saw in *CEftRW,* there are a lot of different ways to meet the same need. Not all of those options will be viable, realistic, and sustainable for each situation, though. We typically think through a few questions in order to determine which activities to focus on when creating an enrichment plan:

What's realistic for the animal?

- Abilities
- Breed-typical tendencies
- Likes and dislikes
- Behavior limitations

What's realistic and sustainable for the human?

- Time
- Money
- Abilities
- Likes and dislikes

What's realistic in the environment?

What is likely to best address the behavior issues and/or goals?

Keep in mind, though, that potential activities aren't just about what you can do with your pet. They are also about what you can do for your pet. Learning canine body language can drastically change how much agency you feel comfortable providing. That's not something you do with your pet, but for them. Speaking with your vet about things to watch out for as they age is something that you do for your pet instead of with them. We are just as much a part of the enrichment equation as they are!

What's realistic for the dog?

Let's first look at the animal in front of us and narrow down options based on who we're working with.

Abilities

Abilities can refer to physical abilities, cognitive abilities, and skills they already have. We should take into consideration factors like mobility, physical health limitations, cognitive limitations (e.g., canine cognitive dysfunction), and anything else that would keep an animal from being able to participate in an activity or cause the animal harm. For example, a dog with joint pain shouldn't be doing puppy pushups or performing high-impact activities like fetch and flirt pole. We'll want to look into lower-impact activities for them, like swimming and weight training.

Be sure to truly look at the dog in front of you and what their limitations are. It's easy to make assumptions about what a dog can and can't do based on their physical or cognitive abilities, but we won't know if those assumptions are true until we observe them. We have met two-legged dogs who have better mobility than many four-legged dogs! We need to make decisions based on observing this particular individual, not based on our assumptions about them.

If your pet does have a physical or cognitive limitation, be sure to speak with a qualified professional about the implications of that diagnosis. Get specific: How much running can they do each day, approximately? What signs should I look for to know if something is too much? How can I expect their needs and abilities to change as their health issue progresses? This is an instance where the potential activity is going to be for our pet instead of with them.

We can also look at the skills they already have that could be used for different activities. For example, food puzzles might be a good mental exercise option for dogs who have already learned how to use them. A dog who hasn't yet learned how to use a food puzzle, however, will likely not benefit as much from them until they've learned how to do so.

Breed-typical tendencies

As we discussed in *CEftRW*, breed tendencies are just that: tendencies. There are retrievers who never got the memo that they should put things in their mouths and terriers who never got the memo that they were made to hunt and kill vermin. However, as we're narrowing down potential activities, we can and should certainly keep breed tendencies in mind, especially if we're seeing those tendencies in the individual in front of us. If they're a terrier exhibiting predatory behaviors, let's try a flirt pole. Scent hound? Scent work. Retriever? Retrieving and putting stuff in their mouths. Herder? Treibball or finding real hoofstock to work if possible. Look at the history of what that breed was originally bred to do and what activity most closely resembles that activity.

> ### A note for mixed breeds
> There has yet to be evidence that breed mixes consistently inherit the breed-typical behavioral tendencies of their purebred ancestors. The best option is to look at the behaviors you see being exhibited by the particular individual you're working with and start with activities that incorporate those behaviors.

Likes and dislikes

We all have preferences, including our pets. Instead of working against their preferences, let's work with them! For example, Allie's dog Oso loves chewing and shredding toys, but isn't a huge fan of playing with them now, except for tug (in his younger days he was more into them). Instead of trying to make fetch happen, Allie and her husband play tug with him for his physical exercise and provide DIY destructible toys for shredding.

Behavior limitations

There may be activities that we would like to do with our dogs or activities that we think they may enjoy, but some facet of their behavior eliminates this possibility. For example, it may not be appropriate to provide food puzzles for dogs who guard food-related items. Or walking may need to be discontinued while a dog is learning skills to mitigate leash reactivity. If an activity is beneficial for one area but detrimental to another, we should avoid it.

What's realistic and sustainable for the human?

We routinely see people get really excited about enrichment activities, training, or behavior modification, only to burn themselves out when they've implemented too many to be sustainable for their daily routine. As Emily says, "If you couldn't do this every day for a year, then it's not sustainable." There are several reasons an activity might not be realistic and sustainable for the human; we'll explore them below.

Time

Going on three-hour walks might be something some dogs would enjoy, but it's probably not going to fit into a lot of people's schedules on a daily basis. We can absolutely keep longer activities in the mix for weekends and when folks have more down time, but we shouldn't rely on them for most of an enrichment plan. Instead of a three-hour walk, we may try flirt pole or fetch to see how 15 minutes of high intensity running compares to a three-hour walk.

Money

A sustainable enrichment plan needs to be budget-friendly, and that will differ depending on the situation. We run into this particular factor quite often when working with dogs who have separation-related problems. While doggy daycare five days a week may be a great management strategy for the behavior issue, it just doesn't fit into a lot of people's budgets. We then need to get creative with cheaper ways to not leave the dog alone, like enlisting the help of friends, family, neighbors, and community members on a rotating schedule so no one person has to bear the brunt of the management plan.

Abilities

Like we discussed regarding our pets above, different people will have different physical and cognitive abilities as well as different skills. We both have chronic illnesses, so running daily is definitely not sustainable in our enrichment plans! We instead opt for physical activities that don't require as much on the human end, like long-distance targeting or recalls, flirt pole games, letting the dogs wear each other out (and oh boy, do they ever!), or simply chucking treats down a hallway.

We need to be mindful of choosing activities that currently work for our abilities and skill set, not where we hope to be in the future. We've seen a number of people who get in over their heads when they adopt a high-energy dog in the hope that the dog will help them get more exercise. If you're currently not able to keep up with them, chances are there are going to be a lot of growing pains to be able to do so — if you even get there at all.

As with our pets, we also need to be mindful of the skill set the human currently has. Someone who has absolutely no experience with training probably shouldn't add something more training intensive like Treibball into their current enrichment plan. Luckily for us, there are many activities that do not require a whole lot of skill on the human end! Instead of Treibball for a herding breed, we could see if they'd like to herd something like a soccer ball in a more freeform way than within the confines of a sport.

Likes and dislikes

While meeting your dog's needs is important, we also need to be mindful of the human's needs. There are many times when we are speaking with a client and dissecting an enrichment plan to figure out what's working and what's not working, only to discover that the client is doing an activity because they enjoy it even if it's "not working." If that's the case, and as long as it's not detrimental to the needs of the dog and their goals, keep it! Again, the human is just as much a part of the equation as the animal is. Our likes and dislikes should come into play when creating an enrichment plan, especially because people are more likely to do something when they enjoy doing it. If you love walking with your dog and they appear to enjoy it even though it's not fulfilling their physical or mental exercise needs, go for it.

The caveat to this is that there will be times that we have to do things even if we don't enjoy them. Going to the vet does not usually make the list of "most fun things to do with your dog," but it's a necessity nonetheless. There will be times when a less-than-fun activity is required in order to meet the needs of the animal or the behavior goals (we're looking at you, separation anxiety exercises).

What's realistic in the environment?

Allie, who lives in the Chicagoland area, has seen a number of times where someone adopts a high-energy dog in the summer and runs several miles per day with them, only to be stymied in the winter on how to provide their dog with enough physical activity. Running several miles per day outside is only realistic part of the year in her area (for most runners and their dogs, at least).

Off-leash hiking is fantastic for those who live in remote areas, but it's simply not safe in a city. Flirt pole requires quite a bit of space for any dog over toy-sized, as does agility. Swimming options are limited for those living in a desert. Giant breed-sized crates don't fit in most apartments. Food puzzles require storage. Our environment will limit what's possible, and that's okay. We can adapt and tweak exercises to make them more realistic for the environment we live in.

What is likely to best address the behavior issues and/or goals?

If the measure of a good enrichment plan is being able to meet our behavioral goals, then we need to choose activities that will help us do that! Counterconditioning is unlikely to be on most people's enrichment activities list, but it's necessary if we're going to address fear- and anxiety-related behaviors. We need to look at what activities will likely work well to address our goals, and bonus points if it can fit multiple bills. For example, if we have a dog who has both attention-seeking behaviors on days where their human can't walk them for long and is chasing the cat, flirt pole is a great option to address both of those behaviors.

Step 5: Prioritize Activities

Now that we have our list of potential activities, it's time to prioritize them so we can start seeing success as quickly as possible. We typically prioritize activities using the following steps:

1. Across the Board or Small Step Big Win
2. Small Step Big Win or Across the Board
3. Laying the Foundation
4. Building on the Foundation

> **Why are numbers 1 and 2 essentially the same thing?**
> Because both Across the Board and Small Step Big Win are about simple activities and easy wins, we often do activities that fit into each of those categories simultaneously or go back and forth between those two categories. Which comes first is going to be dependent on the situation, so keeping both categories in both steps felt like the easiest way to illustrate that this part is more fluid. Either way, we need to prioritize these two categories of activities before we start any foundational training.

Across the Board
This step refers to big-picture activities that are going to affect multiple categories for the better. This is an activity that's going to give you a lot of bang for your buck and create a lot of easy wins. You'll see change across the board. For our fellow behavior consultants, this activity is great for generating client buy-in because they'll be able to easily see the effects from one simple activity. Scent work is one of our favorite Across the Board activities because it can affect the mental stimulation, sensory stimulation, species-typical behaviors, foraging, and even calming categories.

Small Step Big Win
Oftentimes the needs in a category are almost met, and we just need to make one little tweak. It's when you find yourself saying, "There's a small or simple action that we could take that will catapult our results in this one particular category." That's what the Small Step Big Win step is for. This step refers to those little tweaks that will bump a category up from "Room for Growth" to "Likely." An example of this is putting poisonous medications out of your pet's reach to improve the safety category. This is another great option for generating client buy-in, because it's also about easy wins. Management often falls into this step.

Laying the Foundation

At this stage we've addressed most of what we can do using small or simple activities, including management, so in the next phase(s) of the enrichment plan we need to establish foundation skills that we can build upon to use when and where we need them. We typically categorize these as techniques that either the human or the animal needs to learn to do proficiently in order to be effective. For example, most people and pets can muddle through a "Find it" exercise where they toss food on the ground for their pets to find but would need to learn some skills to make it through an agility course effectively and safely.

Laying the foundation includes the mechanics of the activity for both the human and animal, teaching the pet the activity in low-stress or low-difficulty situations, and starting to build the animal's and human's reinforcement histories with activities in easier situations to be able to incorporate into more difficult situations later.

Typical training and behavior modification techniques usually fall into this category. But we can also teach our pets other skills, like how to use food puzzles, how to play more politely with conspecifics, and how to relax.

Building on the Foundation

After we've laid and built a solid foundation, in all subsequent phases of the enrichment plan we can build upon that foundation by incorporating those skills into real-life situations and use them as we wanted to. We can also build other skills that rely on the competent performance of foundational skills. For example, we might use a foundational skill like targeting to teach more advanced skills like a solid recall and cooperative care behaviors.

Step 6: Develop a Plan of Action

We know what activities we want to incorporate into our enrichment plan and the order that we'd like to implement them, but we need to make a few more decisions to be as strategic as possible before we get started. Namely, we'll be looking at four of the five Ws. We'll use an example of Allie's dog, Oso, here to illustrate these decisions, but note that these decisions were not the first iteration of his enrichment plan. These are decisions that have been made after several trial-and-error efforts and observation.

Who

If you and your dog live alone, you can probably skip this one. If there are multiple people in the household, you'll want to incorporate this decision into your plan. A plan is great, but without knowing who is going to enact what, it can fall by the wayside. It's best to get really specific to help everyone involved to be more effective with actual implementation. Decide who is going to take on which responsibilities, including planning, implementation, and documentation.

Your dog may also want a say in this! We mentioned earlier that Allie's household meets Oso's physical exercise needs through playing tug. Specifically, though, he doesn't really care to play that game with Allie, only her partner. It's more fun to play that particular game with one person over the other. But when it comes to cuddling before bedtime or when he's scared of something, he often prefers Allie. You may find that your pet decides who they want to implement certain activities.

What

We already know what activities we want to prioritize first and what our goals are. In the next section we'll discuss how to track progress, which should also be included in your plan of action. That way we know what we're testing, what effect we're hoping to see, and what we're looking for to determine if we're seeing that effect.

Example: The physical exercise activity that best meets Oso's needs within his regular environment is tug, evidenced by a decrease in undesirable behaviors.

One more note here: Test for one activity at a time when you can. There will be times where this is harder or inadvisable, as is the case with management, where we usually need to implement multiple strategies simultaneously to prevent undesirable behaviors from being rehearsed. When a dog with various anxiety-related behaviors comes to a consultant, we'll ask them to enact a fairly strict management plan, which inevitably includes many changes at the same time and often affects several enrichment categories at the same time. That's a situation in which safety trumps everything else, like we saw with agency (in this case it may be physical and/or emotional well-being that we're protecting).

When we have the luxury, though, we should implement one activity at a time. When you try a bunch of things at the same time and see success, you don't know which of those is actually successful. It may be all of them, or the combination of those activities. Or, oftentimes, it's only a couple of those things that are actually successful. But because we don't know which is and isn't, people can get stuck doing a lot more than they need to do.

When

Timing is important! Although we typically talk about needs on a larger scale, remember that needs change throughout the day on a smaller scale. This is true for us as well. If it's 1 a.m., then sleep is probably the activity we need, but earlier in the day we may require physical exercise. If we try to exercise a dog when they require sleep, that exercise will not be as effective as it would be at a different time of day. Conversely, if you try to train a dog when they need a nap, they'll be less motivated to work with you.

Observe your dog's behavior throughout the day to see when they are naturally more energetic or tired. Is there a particular time of day when you're seeing more or fewer instances of those undesirable behaviors? Try to implement your activities shortly before those "witching hours" where your dog is more inclined to perform undesirable behaviors. As we discussed in *CEftRW* dogs are crepuscular, meaning they are typically most active around dawn and dusk, and typically rest during the day and sleep throughout the night. Keep this in mind if you're unsure when to start implementing certain activities.

Example: Tug must be played after 4:30 p.m. to mitigate Oso's 7:30 p.m. witching hour. If played earlier in the day, there is no impact on evening behavior.

We'll throw duration into this category since we're talking about time. There are plenty of instances where an activity is only effective after a certain duration. We can probably all agree that 30 seconds of fetch isn't tiring. As such, duration needs to be a factor in our plan of action as well.

Example: Oso needs at least five minutes of tug to see an appreciable decrease in undesirable evening behavior.

In addition to duration, frequency is another aspect of timing. There are some activities that may be most beneficial when done daily, but there are others that may only have to happen a few times a week or even less frequently.

Example: On days when Oso gets additional forms of physical exercise, we don't play tug, so that specific activity does not need to be done daily to reach our goals.

Another aspect of the "when" category is deciding how long you're going to try something before moving on. Trying something once and moving on is rarely effective. Behavior change involves change over time. Have an idea of how long to try an activity before tweaking it or declaring it "ineffective" for this particular dog in this particular time of their life. Three days would be as short as we'd suggest, though two weeks is our standard. Both of those amounts of time are somewhat arbitrary, though, so do not hold them as hard and fast rules. The only exception is if something is worsening the behavior. In that case, stop immediately and go back to the drawing board.

Where

The more obvious part of "where" is the physical location of where the activities will take place. If swimming is on your list, where will you take them? If it's an indoor pool, have you scheduled a time slot to bring your dog in? If you end up not loving that location, is there a backup? Have an idea of where you will be performing any enrichment activities so that piece of the puzzle doesn't stymie you when you go to actually implement.

The other part of "where" is deciding the context in which your dog can engage with these activities. This is especially important in the Laying the Foundation and Building stages of prioritization, because your success will be tied to the situations in which you're working. Keep in mind that the animal's needs will change depending on the situation, too, so they will likely have some say in this!

Example: Oso will play tug in the living room where the rug gives him the best traction but also lets his humans still watch TV while playing with him. He will decline play if anyone is eating.

To recap, consider the following factors when developing your plan of action:

Who:

- Human preference for implementing
- Dog preference for implementing

What:

- What one thing we're testing
- What our goals are
- What we're using to measure progress

When:

- Time of day
- Duration
- Frequency
- How long we'll try it for

Where:

- Physical location
- Types of situations

Step 7: Implement and Document

So now you have an idea of what you want to do with your dog (or your client's dog, or your dog facility) now, and you're excited to get started. That's great!

An important part of implementation is objectively measuring our progress as we go.

This is important because we humans aren't great at objective observation. We are, all of us, subject to cognitive biases, which are errors in thinking when we process and interpret information from the world around us. This isn't a character flaw, and it doesn't mean you're bad or stupid. It just means you're human. It happens to all of us. Even the most educated people on earth still succumb to **cognitive biases**. We all see the world through the filter of our learning history, our beliefs, our worldview, our unresolved traumas, and how we're feeling in that moment. Even seemingly simple things like hunger, thirst, fatigue, distraction, pain, and irritability or excitement can influence how we perceive what is happening.

For this reason, data collection is important. We know that can sound scary and very scientific — and for zoos, aviaries, and aquariums it can get pretty intensive! — but all it really means is that we have to find some ways to easily track overt behaviors so that we can look at how those behaviors change over time, independently of how we feel at any given moment. We don't have to approach data collection with the depth and rigor of a behavior analyst; there are simpler ways to achieve our goals.

We help our clients to do this simple data collection through what we call "progress logs." And most of the time, clients find that it's a sustainable way to objectively track progress. And it sure is exciting and rewarding to see the progress you make over time!

In order to make a progress log, we first need to start by creating what we call an "intensity chart" for each behavior issue you want to change. A behavior issue usually includes multiple behaviors.

For example, this is an intensity chart that Emily created for some caregivers who were working with a dog at a sanctuary and were having difficulty gauging their own progress with the dog.

Jumpy/Mouthy Behaviors
Level 1: Puts paws on people but doesn't push or mouth.
Level 2: Jumps up, possibly with a gentle push. May knock a child down.
Level 3: Jumps up repeatedly and/or with a moderate shove. May or may not be putting skin and objects in mouth, but without applying pressure. May knock down a child or frail adult.
Level 4: Jumps up and shoves or grabs enough to knock a healthy adult off balance. Applied slight to moderate pressure when mouthing.
Level 5: Jumps up and shoves or grabs enough to knock a healthy adult off balance. Applies enough pressure to cause marks on the skin and grabs or pulls objects attached to a person.
Level 6: Jumps up and shoves or grabs enough to knock a healthy adult off balance. Applies enough pressure to bruise or break the skin, and will tear clothing and break/damage objects attached to person.

These six sets of behaviors were the six variations of this jumpy-mouthy issue that they had observed and were working to address with this particular dog.

At first, the caregivers didn't think they were making any progress with the dog because he was still jumping and mouthing sometimes, whereas Emily had noticed quite a bit of improvement in his behavior. When they had started, he was all 6s, all the time. By the time she made this intensity chart for them, he was mostly 0s, sometimes 1s, and every so often a 2 or a 3.

After she made this chart for them and had them start writing down the number that corresponded with the behavior they observed, they realized how much progress they had actually made, and suddenly felt a lot better about the process!

We typically have clients create their intensity charts and set up their progress logs when we first start working together. That way they start recording the behaviors at the very beginning, before we've started making any changes that might impact the behavior. As we implement each phase of the enrichment plan, reviewing the progress logs allows us and our clients to see exactly how much the behaviors have changed as a result of our current strategies. Do we need to tweak what we're doing in this current phase? Or are we ready to move on to the next phase? Documenting the behaviors we see while we're implementing the plan makes implementation more efficient, because we can see the actual impact of what we're doing as we're doing it, which means we can course correct right away instead of wasting time on ineffective strategies.

How to create your own intensity chart
1. Write out every variation of the behavior issue you've seen your dog exhibit. Remember to include only overt behaviors, not labels or constructs! The point of this exercise is to track the dog's actions, not our guesses at what's going on inside their heads.

2. Assign a number to each set of behaviors in order of intensity, where 1 = the lowest intensity, and it goes up from there. *You do not have to have six levels.* The chart above is just an example. We've had clients who only had four levels of intensity on their charts, and other clients who've had 20-plus. It depends on the dog and the behaviors you're observing.

You can do the exact same thing for desirable behaviors you're hoping to see more of, too! In fact, we encourage you to!

Once you have all the intensity charts you need, you can start using a progress log.

How to create your own progress log
1. Create a calendar that is just for tracking your progress and nothing else. We want it to be as uncluttered as possible. We prefer to use Google Calendar, because we can easily access it from all our devices

and multiple people who are working with the same animal(s) can all have equally easy access. But of course, use whatever calendar system you prefer, whether it's another digital calendar app or a good old fashioned paper calendar.

2. Create a color-coding system for each intensity chart you have created.

3. When you observe a set of behaviors in the context in which you want to change them, write the corresponding number from that intensity chart in your calendar in the corresponding color.

4. If you don't see the behavior in that context at all, you can choose to either use a 0, or leave it blank (like kind of a "no news is good news" default). For example, in the example above, if anyone walked into the dog's run and he didn't jump or mouth at all, the caregivers would put a zero in his chart. Some people find it rewarding to slap that 0 down in their calendars, whereas others find it more convenient to just not mess with the calendar at all unless they see something noteworthy. Another consideration is that if you sometimes forget to document a behavior you see, you may want to use 0s to differentiate between when you remembered to document the absence of the undesirable behavior versus when you forgot to document anything at all. We've seen both ways work well so, again, it's up to you!

It takes just a few seconds to write a number in a calendar, so it doesn't add much time or effort to your day. But after a few weeks of documentation, it is so rewarding to look at your calendar and be able to see at a glance how much progress you've made. It helps with morale, especially on those days when you've had a small setback and it feels like you've done all that work for nothing! But conversely, it also helps if you're not seeing those numbers change much at all. That tells us that we can stop wasting time and energy on an ineffective strategy so that we can reassess, readdress, and try again!

Get help if need be
If the undesirable behaviors are getting worse during the implementation process, stop and seek help from someone who knows more than you do!

Step 8: Reassess, Readdress, and Do It Again

You've implemented your plan and have information about how well your plan is working. It's now time to reassess your enrichment plan based on the information that you gathered during the implementation step. What changes do you need to make to this current step before moving on? Or can you move on to the next step now? If you didn't reach the goal you were hoping to, you'll need to readdress your plan and try it again. If you did reach your current goal, you can move on to the next one.

What to try next

If you saw some success with what you tried but not as much as you'd hoped, go back to the "Develop a Plan of Action" step and adjust the factors involved there. If something is partially working, it's more worthwhile to tweak that to see if it can completely work instead of scrapping it.

If you saw no success with what you tried, consider shelving that activity and either moving on to something else within that category or another category altogether. Because our pets can't talk in human language with us to tell us what they need, we sometimes need to take a trial-and-error approach until we get it right. Be patient and, when in doubt, speak with someone more experienced than you.

What if I reach all my goals?

Well done! Give yourself a pat on the back. Keep in mind, though, that you're never truly done. Needs are lifelong, and what we need changes as we age and environments change. You may be done for now, with this most recent set of goals, but you'll need to readdress your pet's enrichment plan at some point in the future.

What if I didn't reach all my goals but I want to stop here?

That's also okay. We've said throughout this workbook that your needs are just as important as your pet's needs. If you haven't reached all your goals but your pet is in a place where they and others are safe and they generally have good physical, emotional, and behavioral well-being, you can still say that you've earned a break from pushing forward. Part of a sustainable plan is knowing when you can take a break from trying new things and just enjoy the success you and your pet have achieved to this point.

Troubleshooting

Invariably, when we try to do something involving living, sentient beings, things don't always go as planned. Our tendency as human beings is to either say: a) I can't do this, b) my dog can't do/doesn't like/doesn't care about this, or c) this approach doesn't work.

These responses are understandable but not especially productive. Instead, we want to nurture a sense of curiosity and critical thinking in our readers. When something isn't working out as well as we thought it should, think of it as less of a setback and more of an opportunity to learn new things via troubleshooting. So let's talk about some of the most common troubleshooting issues we encounter when working with pet parents and professionals on creating and implementing an enrichment plan.

"This is too complicated. I want something simpler."
Let's talk about simplicity. One of the alluring promises that some trainers offer is a quick fix with a simple solution. We wholeheartedly agree with those trainers that our clients are not professionals, and therefore they should be given simple steps that they can easily master on their journey toward a solution. Where we diverge is in believing that simplicity is our priority above all else, and that everything can — or should — be a simple fix, at any cost to the dog.

Intentionally ignoring or being ignorant of the multiple complex systems that impact behavior — and therefore our enrichment strategies — doesn't make those complexities cease to exist. We can't, and shouldn't, try to wish away those complexities because we don't want to deal with them, or don't want our clients to have to deal with them.

However, the good news is that we don't have to take on all those complexities in one huge lump. We can make this easier on ourselves and our clients by doing a two-step process:

1. What is the simplest possible solution to this problem without compromising the dog's welfare or ignoring important factors?
2. When it isn't simple, how can I break it up into a series of simple steps?

We frequently get feedback from our clients about how surprised they are at how simple the exercises we've given them are. That's because we have learned how to simplify as much as possible, and when we can't do that, we break the big, complex thing into smaller, simpler steps.

In other words, instead of dismissing the complexities, we break them down into a series of simplicities.

If you're a professional and you haven't learned how to do that yet, that's okay! It's a normal part of the learning process. When we don't know much, we tend to oversimplify. When we start to learn something (or when we're burned out), we tend to overexplain and overcomplicate it. As we learn more, we get better at breaking it down into simple — but precise! — steps.

The basic process is this: If it's too difficult or overwhelming, break it up into smaller steps. If the first step is still too difficult or overwhelming, break that step up into smaller steps. Repeat this process until you get to a step that feels doable.

Simplifying: an example
Client feels overwhelmed by teaching their dog how to scatter-feed in the yard unattended.

- First, teach "Find it"
- Then do "Find it" in the yard
- When the dog can find all the pieces without help, use more food over a larger patch of grass
- Continue increasing the amount of food and the area you're scattering it until he can use the whole yard to find his whole meal
- Practice casually walking around the yard while the dog eats
- Practice walking in and out the back door
- Practice staying inside for longer periods of time
- Practice staying inside the whole time with the door open
- Practice staying inside the whole time with the door closed

"My client doesn't want to bother with enrichment; they just want quick solutions."
First things first: We rarely tell our clients that they have to use enrichment. It's simply not necessary, and framing the conversation like, "I'm going to give you a training plan and an enrichment plan" makes them feel like you're doubling their workload. In reality, when we're using an enrichment framework to address maladaptive behaviors, the training plan is a part of enrichment. Unless the client already knows about enrichment and wants to talk about it, we simply give them their client worksheets with the current steps for them to focus on. All of it is enrichment, and some of that enrichment involves training, but for the client it's just the plan. So a big part of client resistance is because of how we're framing the conversation; change the conversation and it will change their perception.

Secondly: When a client is feeling a sense of urgency, they are communicating to you that they have pain points that feel unmanageable to them. They may not always know how to put it into words, or they may feel afraid to share that with you, so sometimes this requires asking a series of nonjudgmental questions to help them articulate their pain points.

One of the things that trainers who offer quick-fix solutions do very well — and something that the science-and-ethics-based community could stand to learn a lot from them — is alleviating those pain points quickly. Of course, we know that meeting needs isn't often a fast process, and promising a quick fix is unethical, but if we want our clients to be willing and able to shift their mindset from just making an annoying problem go away to creating a lifestyle of enrichment for them and their pets, the very first thing we have to do is quickly alleviate those pain points. This is where that Small Step Big Win comes in extremely handy. After alleviating that pain point, your client and their dog will feel safe and comfortable enough to stick around for the long-term solutions addressing all of the unmet needs.

Quick fixes: an example
Emily had a client with an anxious, blind dog who was reactive to people in the home. The client's best friend was coming into town two weeks after Emily started working with them and was staying with them for two weeks. The client needed a quick solution to prevent their dog from reacting to their houseguest for two weeks straight. The

pain point was a sense of urgency about getting the dog to peacefully coexist with their houseguest in a very short period of time. This was Emily's quick fix approach to alleviating the client's most urgent pain point:

- Create a management strategy that prevents the dog from interacting with the guest except during specified times.
- Teach "Find it," which most dogs learn in a matter of minutes. Practice every day for just a few minutes between now and when the houseguest arrives.
- Play "Find it" at a distance from the guest at which the dog is aware of the guest but not too stressed to play the game.
- Gradually decrease the distance at which the dog is willing to play the game in the company of the guest.

Because Emily was able to quickly alleviate the client's urgent pain point, the client was then willing and able to commit to the longer-term process of helping her dog in more lasting and holistic ways.

"I'm not quite sure what needs aren't being met."

In almost every situation where the unmet need is unclear, we can get a clearer picture by getting a more thorough history and doing a more thorough and methodical inventory. As we've mentioned several times throughout this workbook, we rarely use the enrichment chart or any of these worksheets ourselves. We do this in our heads most of the time. But when something about the behavior isn't clear or our initial approach didn't seem to be working, we'll use these tools to help us systematically walk through the client's history so we can get a clearer picture of which needs aren't being sufficiently met. It's also really important to look at the behavior in context! Sometimes you'll get clues based on when and where the behavior happens, and what else is going on at the time.

Identifying needs: an example

Emily had another client whose dog had a variety of behavior issues, one of which was barking at the downstairs roommate when she got home from work. They had successfully worked through most of the issues, but the stairs-barking behavior persisted.

Relevant history initially provided:

- Dog had bitten the roommate when she tried to pick him up.
- Undesirable behavior: Dog stands at the top of the stairs barking at the roommate when he hears her walk through the front door downstairs.
- Observed body language: Conflicted. Definite stress signals present, but unclear as to whether they were distress or eustress.

Standard reactivity protocols weren't affecting behavior change in a reasonable period of time (two weeks), so they went back through the history together.

New and relevant information gleaned:

- Dog and roommate got along well aside from handling issues, which was not clearly communicated in the initial history.
- Dog never went downstairs on his own. His owner always carried him.
- Stairs were slippery hardwood and the dog's nails were long.

It became apparent that the unidentified unmet needs were:

- Security (dog was hesitant to walk down the stairs because of the slippery surface)
- Hygiene (traction was compromised by long nails)
- Social interaction (dog wanted to greet roommate but couldn't)
- Agency (dog did not have the choice to move freely between spaces!)

What Emily had initially mistaken for fear reactivity turned out to be barrier frustration, which was easily addressed by trimming the dog's nails and providing a no-slip surface on the stairs so the dog could easily walk down on his own to greet the roommate any time she came home.

"What do I do when the client and their dog have opposing needs?"

We understand that this can frequently feel like it's the case, but it rarely actually is. We humans tend to fall prey to **false dichotomies** — where we think there are only two options, so we must pick one of those two options. Fortunately, the reality is that there are usually multiple options that we just haven't thought of yet.

When it seems like the only two options are either help the client or help the dog, that's probably an opportunity to go back to the needs checklist and enrichment chart and identify exactly what the needs are. This is important because usually when it feels like the client and the dog have mutually exclusive needs, it's just the way in which we're trying to meet the need that is mutually exclusive.

Conflicting needs: an example

The belief that either you use the prong collar to meet the client's needs of safety and security, or you ditch the prong collar to meet the dog's needs of security, sensory stimulation, and agency is almost always a false dichotomy. Of course, we could always look into alternative management tools that might be less aversive to the dog (might be! Only the dog can decide that, and the only way to know would be to observe the outcome!), such as front-clip harnesses or head halters. But the better question is: Why are we walking the dog when the dog clearly doesn't yet have the skills to walk safely on leash without the threat of discomfort from metal prongs? What need are we trying to meet by walking the dog? Typically, the answer is physical and/or mental exercise. Okay, so what other ways can we meet the dog's physical and mental exercise needs while we're teaching the dog better leash-walking skills?

By taking this approach, we can almost always remove the perceived conflict and meet the needs of both client and dog.

That said, sometimes there really isn't another option. It really is the client's needs versus the dog's needs. In those rare instances, the client's needs always come first. This is one of those "put on your own oxygen mask first" scenarios. The client can't go on to meet their dog's needs if their own needs aren't being met first.

Prioritizing the client's needs: an example

Let's stick with the subject of prong collars, since that's what we discussed above. A friend and colleague of Emily's told her a story once of the only time she'd ever recommended a prong collar to a client, and it has since become a favorite thought experiment that Emily gives to her students. The client had adopted a 200-pound Neapolitan Mastiff to be trained as her service dog for balance issues. But the dog came to her completely untrained, and she lived in a third-floor condo. She had to take the dog down three flights of stairs multiple times per day so the dog could go to the bathroom, but he would drag her down the stairs, especially first thing in the morning. Since she already had balance issues, he dragged her off her feet, and she fell and broke her arm. Emily's colleague tried as many other options as she could think of first, but none of them were effective at meeting her client's needs for safety. So, she had the client use a prong collar at first to protect the client's safety while they trained the dog to have better walking skills. Within a month they didn't need the prong collar anymore because the dog had learned solid loose-leash walking skills without needing the collar. It was a suboptimal situation where they needed a suboptimal solution for a very short period of time until they could work on a better long-term solution.

But again! This was an extraordinary (and extraordinarily rare) circumstance that most of us won't ever encounter in our careers. In almost every case, we can find a way to meet both the client's and the dog's needs without violating the needs of the other.

"I don't have enough time!"

Friends: Allow us to introduce you to the magic that is prepping in bulk. You will spend less time per item if you set yourself up to make multiples of that thing at a time than if you prep a new one every day. If you're making perishable items like stuffed Kongs and marrow bones, home-cooked food, or pupsicles, invest in a small deep freezer and make a week or a month's worth at a time. If you make non-perishable toys, invest in a toy box so you can spend a few hours filling the box. Emily and Allie usually do their prep for the week or the month on one of their weekends, or in the evenings while watching TV or listening to audiobooks or podcasts.

Alternatively, if your dog enjoys tearing up cardboard but doesn't eat the cardboard, make a "recycle bin" just for your dog and put any safe, appropriate cardboard boxes in their recycle bin. Emily does this with her dogs and it's just about the cutest thing to watch them explore the new boxes that magically appeared in their recycle bin, pick one that they want to destroy, and then take it to their favorite relaxation station for some good old shredding fun. Emily never puts out cardboard that has food on it (e.g., used pizza boxes) or cardboard that has adhesives on it (remove tape first!), but otherwise, any cardboard that ends up in the doggo recycle bin is fair game for Copper and Brie! The best part is that it requires next to zero effort on Emily's part. It takes as much time as it would take to put it in an actual recycling bin and sweeping up the shredded pieces takes as much time as it would always take to sweep the floor. The dogs have hours of fun, and it costs Emily practically nothing.

If the time constraint is the outings you take your dog on, go back to your needs checklist and enrichment chart and remember what your goal is for those outings. Is there a way to meet the same needs with shorter or less frequent outings, either by replacing some of that with in-home activities, or recruiting another family member to share in those responsibilities, or finding activities that will give you more bang for your buck? Or could you just reduce the outings because the dog is fine with less?

The same is true for training: Do you *need* to spend as much time training as you do, or do you *feel like* you need to?

A lot of the time we find that both clients and professionals get overwhelmed because they feel like they aren't doing enough, even though they're already doing more than they can handle, but they're only doing that much because they feel like they need to, not because they actually do. Remember our friend from the book who joked about having CPUPS? This is one of those situations. Remember: Don't let ideology get in the way of observation. If your dog is still physically, behaviorally, and emotionally healthy with doing less, do less.

Our friend and colleague Nancy Tucker gives a presentation at conferences called "The Good Enough Dog," and we'd like to extend that to "The Good Enough Human." Your enrichment plan will probably never be perfect. Ours sure isn't! But if everyone in the home is living harmoniously and everyone's needs are mostly being met, that's good enough.

Not enough time: an example
A client with an adolescent Sheepadoodle was walking him six to eight times a day and additionally playing with him several hours a day. They understandably felt overwhelmed and felt like their entire lives revolved around their dog, which impacted their quality of life.

Our plan:

- We reduced number of necessary walks by rearranging the schedule and improving the quality of the walks for both dog and human.
- We swapped out most of the training-just-for-mental-stimulation sessions for training functional behaviors such as:
    - Our version of the relaxation protocol
    - Using the relaxation protocol to teach the dog more independence, so he could not only self-regulate when he was amped up, but also so that he could contentedly chew on a toy by himself without needing his owners' undivided attention
    - Some skills to address the jumpy-mouthy attention-seeking behaviors that formerly elicited interaction from the owners
- We reduced the number and duration of play periods by incorporating scent work and flirt pole to wear him out faster

At the time of this writing, six weeks after we started, they are down to three walks per day, three to four significantly shorter play sessions a day, three training sessions of 2 to 10 minutes per day, and a dog who can seek rest periods on his own, entertain himself for long periods of time, and can settle on a mat at dog-friendly patio restaurants while his owners enjoy a meal together.

"Finding ways to keep providing novelty is exhausting."

Our question to you, like the one above, is: Do you have to, or do you feel like you have to? Novelty in enrichment is frequently overblown in the pet community. Yes, novelty is good for mental stimulation or sensory stimulation — *to an extent*. But most of the time we find that people are waaaaay overdoing it out of a sense of guilt or duty. In reality, it's almost never a main focus in a descriptive, goal-oriented enrichment plan. Zoos and aviaries commonly have a weekly rotation of the same seven items, and that is novelty enough for the animals in their care.

Novelty: an example

The crows at a wildlife rehab where Emily worked had a weekly schedule for "novel" food items to explore and enjoy in addition to their regular meals:

- Monday: raw rib bones
- Tuesday: peanut butter and jelly sandwiches
- Wednesday: seasonal veggie salad
- Thursday: live crickets
- Friday: homemade mini "pizzas"
- Saturday: baked potatoes stuffed with mealworms
- Sunday: "potluck" (caregivers would bring in whatever crow-appropriate leftovers they had)

That was, really, the only novelty the crows were given aside from the natural fluctuations of life in outdoor aviaries — and yet they were happy, healthy, well-adjusted birds.

Emily doesn't give much thought to novelty, either. The most novelty her animals get is whatever food scraps are safe and appropriate for them to eat from her meals that day, and the car rides to different places she and her partner take them in the evenings. Since Brie was a feral dog and never really became a fan of city life, she gets stressed out when she goes to places where there are a lot of strangers, but she's relaxed and happy to go on car rides and watch strangers from the safety of the car. That's pretty much it. The dogs are fixtures at a variety of drive-through coffee shops around town, where they sometimes — but not always! — get Scooby Snacks or Puppercinos. But otherwise, there isn't an abundance of novelty in their lives.

Remember: Enrichment is about meeting their needs, so they are physically, behaviorally, and emotionally healthy enough to perform species-typical behaviors in safe, healthy, and appropriate ways. If that is our goal, whatever novelty or excitement arises from that process is a byproduct, not the main focus.

Enrichment Protocol Case Study

Now let's showcase the steps we outlined in this workbook using an example of a dog with serious maladaptive behaviors who Allie worked with. We'll show you how to use the Pet Harmony Enrichment Framework via an in-depth breakdown of every part of the process. Please note, we do not actually write all of this out for our clients, or even ourselves. That would take forever, and no one wants to read a behavior modification plan that's 20 pages long. While we've outlined all the steps here in writing, we typically do these in our head unless we're absolutely stuck or someone really wants to see it all laid out step-by-step (which is rare). We're breaking it down into tiny pieces to show you how to go about all this if you do not yet have the skills to do it in your head.

And one more thing. The case study you're about to read was a real client of Allie's and the behaviors outlined were absolutely real. However, that was two years before the writing of this workbook, and a lot of little details were lost along the way. Although Allie has endeavored to recount things as accurately as possible, her memory isn't perfect, so we're taking some liberties here out of necessity.

Ruby

Ruby was a 2ish-year-old, spayed female Bull Terrier. She was found as a stray, left unclaimed in animal control, transferred to a rescue organization, and lived with one foster home before being adopted by her new family.

Her foster family reported that she was fearful of some noises, timid around men and large groups of people, but enjoyed other dogs, women, and kids. She was being treated for worms, and the foster family had trouble getting her to defecate outside, resulting in her frequently defecating in her crate. Ruby slipped out of her collar, resulting in the foster family using a choke chain when outside. The vet reported her clear of worms one week after being adopted. Her foster family reported that Ruby would also occasionally get into the trash.

Ruby had lived with her adoptive family, consisting of a man and woman, for three months when Allie met her. They had recently completed a group training class with a positive reinforcement trainer. They reported that they saw the same fear behaviors that the foster did and that she would get into the trash. After coming home to her new family, they started using a harness instead of the choke chain and no longer had issues with her not defecating outside. She mouthed the woman, which was improving slightly, but seemed to be getting more fearful around the man, especially inside the house.

Step 1: List desirable and undesirable behaviors

Current/existing desirable behaviors:	Current/existing undesirable behaviors:
• Willingly goes to her crate and spends time there • Occasionally plays with resident dog • Runs around at dog park • Listens to training cues • Learns new training cues • Sits more when overstimulated • Is a good eater	• Fearful body language and avoidant of the man • Refuses to walk farther than the yard • Pacing • Trouble relaxing and sleeping if not in her crate • Mouthing woman to the point of bruising, seen in periods of assumed boredom and overstimulation
Goal behaviors: • Decrease anxiety-related behaviors when man is home • Increase relaxation behaviors when man is home • Comfort with man taking her outside to potty on a regular leash • Be able to walk off property • Decrease mouthing as attention-seeking behavior; replace with another behavior • Decrease mouthing as overstimulated behavior; replace with another	• Punctures resident dog during play • Fearful body language in response to noises and voices • Fearful body language when seeing most men • Little exploratory behavior when man is home • Will not leave crate if man is home and woman is not; makes potty training difficult • Gets into the trash

Step 2: Are needs being met?

Here is a checklist that helps assess whether Ruby's needs are being met in various areas of enrichment. Although we recommend the nomenclature provided above, L = likely, IP = in progress, PRFG = potential room for growth, and RFG = room for growth, in this chart Allie simply used a checkmark to indicate "yes," a hyphen for areas that were not applicable, a question mark when she was unable to assess based on the available information, and a box for "no."

Health/Veterinary

- ✓ Regular vet visits
- ✓ Up to date on vaccinations or the equivalent
- – Pain management if needed
- – Management for physical and mental health concerns: medication, physical therapy, surgery, etc.

Hygiene (remember that this is dependent on breed/ morphology)

- ✓ Appropriate amount of bathing
- ✓ Appropriate skin & coat care
- ? Ear cleaning
- ? Nail trims
- ? Dental hygiene
- ✓ Other breed-specific hygiene practices

Diet/Nutrition

- ✓ Appropriate diet for the individual, no health concerns
- ✓ Treats for different scenarios

Physical Exercise

- ❑ Amount of physical activity appreciably reduces fidgeting and other boredom-based behaviors
- ✓ Type of exercise does not compromise physical or mental health (e.g., exacerbates joint disease, causes distress, etc.)

Sensory Stimulation

- ❑ The environment does not elicit stress responses the majority of the time
- ❑ Absence of stereotypical behaviors
- ✓ Opportunities for behavioral diversity

Safety

- ✓ Does not have access to poisonous foods, medications, plants, household items
- ✓ Is not able to interact with animals who would cause bodily or psychological harm, including domestic species, predators, and wildlife
- ✓ Is not able to run into the street or other harmful environments
- ✓ Is not able to interact with humans who would cause bodily or psychological harm
- ✓ Is not exposed to harmful husbandry and training methods and tools

Security

- ✓ Has at least one space in their environment to retreat to where they are exposed to minimal stressors
- ❑ Knows how to move away from stressors when necessary
- ❑ Knows how to investigate novel stimuli
- ❑ Displays fear- or avoidance-related behaviors only in response to reasonable, novel, and/or extraordinary stimuli

Species-Typical/Instinctual Behaviors (including but not limited to: chewing, shredding, digging, barking, chasing, investigating, scavenging, etc.)

- ✓ Has opportunities to display species- or breed-typical behaviors in healthy, safe, and appropriate ways
- ❑ Appropriate species- or breed-typical behaviors are performed with enough frequency and diversity so as to reduce nuisance behaviors

Foraging

- ❑ Knows how to track and/or trail scents
- ❑ Knows how to problem solve in manipulating objects to obtain food
- ✓ The majority of their caloric intake is consumed via foraging
- ❑ Has daily opportunities to perform above behaviors

Social Interaction

✓ Is able to interact with individuals (relative to their level of sociability) in healthy, safe, and appropriate ways

❑ Is not forced to interact with distressing individuals and/or species

❑ Is able to display a diversity of behaviors in the presence of others

❑ Displays appropriate play solicitation behaviors, including breaks and self-regulation

Mental Exercise

✓ Regular opportunities to learn new or expand on existing skills

❑ Regular opportunities to track and/or trail scents

❑ Regular opportunities to problem solve

Independence

❑ Is able to self-entertain

✓ Displays no or minimal distress signals when left alone

❑ Is able to problem solve situations with minimal human guidance

❑ Is able to appropriately communicate needs

Environment

✓ Is provided with predictability, including a predictable schedule/ routines, predictable outcomes, and a reasonably predictable environment (the level of predictability necessary is relative to the individual, based on overall behavioral health)

✓ Regular access to basic necessities

✓ Regular access to opportunities for species-typical behaviors and behavioral diversity

❑ Minimal exposure to chronic or acute stressors

Calming

❑ Takes midday naps

❑ Sleeps soundly at night

❑ Is able to relax in well-known environments

❑ Is able to self-soothe and self-regulate

Current undesirable behaviors	What's driving the current behavior?	Which categories are affected
Avoiding the man	Fear response	Social interaction, security
Refuses to walk farther than the yard	Fear response	Security
Pacing	Distress	Security, environment, sensory stimulation
Trouble relaxing and sleeping if not in her crate	Anxiety	Calming
Mouthing woman: assumed boredom	Sometimes woman redirects with a toy or will yelp	Social interaction, mental exercise, physical exercise
Mouthing woman: assumed overstimulation	Overstimulation	Calming
Punctures resident dog during play	Overstimulation	Social interaction
Fearful body language for noises and voices	Fear response	Environment, Security
Fearful body language when seeing most men	Fear response	Social interaction, security
Little exploratory behavior when man is home	Anxiety	Calming, environment, security, independence
Will not leave crate if man is home and woman is not	Anxiety	Security
Getting into the trash	Garbage is delicious	Foraging, mental exercise

When we look at the current undesirable behaviors, their likely motivations, and the related enrichment categories, we are able to more clearly see which needs are likely being met and which show room for growth.

Aspect of Enrichment	Is this need being met?
Health/Veterinary	Likely
Hygiene	Likely
Diet/Nutrition	Likely
Physical Exercise	Potential Room for Growth
Sensory Stimulation	Room for Growth
Safety	Likely
Security	Room for Growth
Species-Typical Behaviors	Potential Room for Growth
Foraging	Room for Growth
Social Interaction	Room for Growth
Mental Exercise	Potential Room for Growth
Independence	Room for Growth
Environment	Room for Growth
Calming	Room for Growth

Step 3: Are agency needs being met?
Here is a sample of the agency flow chart in action. It examines Ruby's agency when it comes to her health/ veterinary care.

Does Your Pet Have Agency?

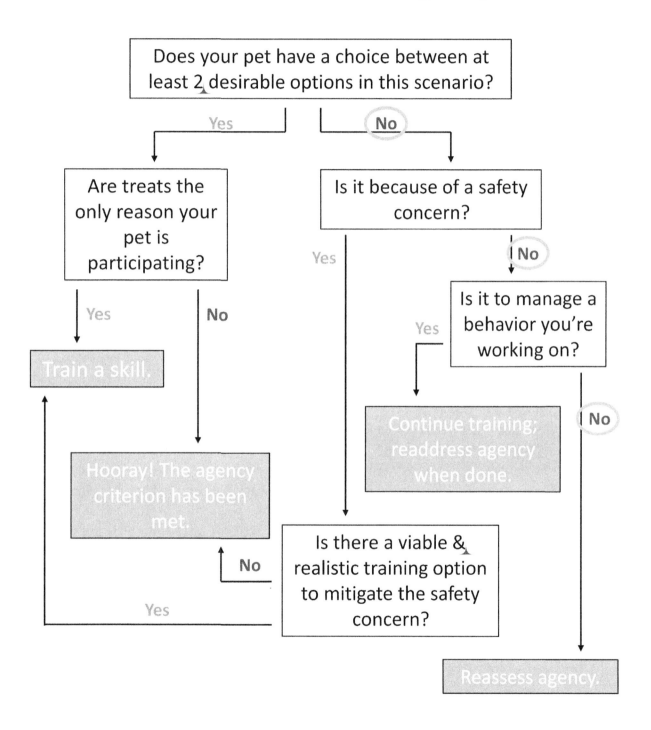

Allie also did a detailed assessment of agency in the other areas of Ruby's life. These are the results.

Hygiene:

- Does your pet have a choice between at least two desirable options in this scenario? No.
  - ○ Scenario: In overall hygiene and grooming practices, Ruby does not have agency.
- Is it because of a safety concern? No.
- Is it to manage a behavior you're working on? No.
- Conclusion: Room for Growth. Ruby needs to be given more agency in hygiene and grooming practices.

Diet/nutrition:

- Does your pet have a choice between at least two desirable options in this scenario? Yes.
  - ○ Scenario: In terms of overall diet and treats, Ruby's parents have done food preference tests and give Ruby a variety of options.
- Are treats the only reason your pet is participating? Not applicable since we're looking at the behavior of eating treats.
- Conclusion: Appropriate. Ruby has choice and control over eating a variety of foods.

Physical exercise:

- Does your pet have a choice between at least two desirable options in this scenario? Yes.
  - ○ Scenario: Ruby's agency regarding exercise fluctuates depending on the day and time of day, but overall, throughout the week, she generally has multiple desirable options for physical exercise.
- Are treats the only reason your pet is participating? No.
- Conclusion: Appropriate. Ruby has plenty of opportunity to choose how to exercise.

Sensory stimulation:

- Does your pet have a choice between at least two desirable options in this scenario? Yes.
  - ○ Scenario: Ruby has the option to go into her crate to escape sensory overwhelm whenever she wants; her parents don't push her to leave the yard, and she can go inside whenever she's ready.
- Are treats the only reason your pet is participating? No.
- Conclusion: Appropriate. Ruby has a way to escape overwhelming sensory input whenever she chooses.

Safety:

- Does your pet have a choice between at least two desirable options in this scenario? Yes.
  - ○ Scenario: In terms of overall safety, Ruby's parents do a good job of protecting her from harm.
- Are treats the only reason your pet is participating? No.
- Conclusion: Appropriate. Ruby is adequately protected from harm.

Security:

- Does your pet have a choice between at least two desirable options in this scenario? No.
  - ○ Scenario: When it comes to feeling secure, sometimes she does have agency (crate: see above), but sometimes she has to get closer to the husband than she is comfortable with due to the layout of their house.
- Is it because of a safety concern? No.

- Is it to manage a behavior you're working on? No.
- Conclusion: Room for Growth. Ruby needs to be given more choice to move away from the husband.

Species-typical behaviors:

- Does your pet have a choice between at least two desirable options in this scenario? No.
  - Scenario: Ruby has a couple of foraging options, but has not tried a lot of other species-typical activities for us to know if she has enough options to perform other species-typical behaviors.
- Is it because of a safety concern? No.
- Is it to manage a behavior you're working on? No.
- Conclusion: Potential Room for Growth. We need to do more sleuthing to determine if Ruby needs more opportunities.

Foraging:

- Does your pet have a choice between at least two desirable options in this scenario? Yes.
  - Scenario: Ruby has plenty of foraging options.
- Are treats the only reason your pet is participating? Not applicable, since the goal is for her to forage for food.
- Conclusion: Appropriate. Ruby has ample opportunities to forage.

Social interaction:

- Does your pet have a choice between at least two desirable options in this scenario? No.
  - Scenario: Ruby does have agency when it comes to dogs, but when it comes to social interaction with humans, there are situations in which the husband needs to take her outside to potty.
- Is it because of a safety concern? Yes, physical health concern from holding urine too long.
- Is there a viable and realistic training option to mitigate the safety concern? Yes.
- Conclusion: Room for Growth. We need to improve her relationship with the husband so she will choose to go on potty walks with him.

Mental exercise:

- Does your pet have a choice between at least two desirable options in this scenario? Yes.
  - Scenario: Overall, Ruby has plenty of mental exercise options.
- Are treats the only reason your pet is participating? No.
- Conclusion: Appropriate. Ruby has ample choices in mental exercise.

Independence:

- Does your pet have a choice between at least two desirable options in this scenario? No.
  - Scenario: Ruby does not have the skills to self-entertain or communicate, which limits her level of independence.
- Is it because of a safety concern? No.
- Is it to manage a behavior you're working on? No.
- Conclusion: Room for Growth. We need to teach Ruby skills that allow her to gain some level of self-sufficiency.

Environment:

- Does your pet have a choice between at least two desirable options in this scenario? No.
  - ○ Scenario: Ruby only feels comfortable in her crate.
- Is it because of a safety concern? No.
- Is it to manage a behavior you're working on? No.
- Conclusion: Room for Growth. Ruby needs to learn how to feel comfortable in many other places.

Calming:

- Does your pet have a choice between at least two desirable options in this scenario? No.
  - ○ Scenario: Ruby has multiple places available to rest, but will only rest in crate.
- Is it because of a safety concern? No.
- Is it to manage a behavior you're working on? No.
- Conclusion: Room for Growth. Ruby needs to be able to rest in multiple places, not just her crate.

Based on the analysis of Ruby's agency across different aspects of enrichment, the below chart provides us a complete picture of where her needs for both enrichment and agency are being met. This will guide us toward certain areas of enrichment to focus on.

Aspect of Enrichment	Is this need being met?	Agency?
Health/Veterinary	Likely	Room for Growth
Hygiene	Likely	Room for Growth
Diet/Nutrition	Likely	Appropriate
Physical Exercise	Potential Room for Growth	Appropriate
Sensory Stimulation	Room for Growth	Appropriate
Safety	Likely	Appropriate
Security	Room for Growth	Room for Growth
Instinctual Behaviors	Potential Room for Growth	Potential Room for Growth
Foraging	Room for Growth	Room for Growth
Social Interaction	Room for Growth	Room for Growth
Mental Exercise	Potential Room for Growth	Potential Room for Growth
Independence	Room for Growth	Room for Growth
Environment	Room for Growth	Room for Growth
Calming	Room for Growth	Room for Growth

Step 4: Potential activities for unmet needs

As a reminder, the categories in which Ruby has room for growth include:

- Physical exercise
- Sensory stimulation
- Security
- Species-typical behaviors
- Foraging
- Social interaction

- Mental exercise
- Independence
- Environment
- Calming

Within the above categories, here is a list of all of the activities that Ruby's owners could use to meet her needs. We have italicized the ones that we believe are most appropriate for her temperament and circumstances.

Physical exercise
- Walks
- Flirt pole
- *Games like tug, fetch, and hide and seek*
- Swimming
- Dog Sports
- *Playing with other dogs*

Sensory stimulation
- *Scent games like scent tubes, scatter feeding, or K9 Nosework*
- *Sniffaris*
- Adventure walks/adventure boxes
- *Massage, T-Touch, Jin Shin Jyutsu, etc.*
- *Texture, food, or toy preference tests*
- *Visual masking via Calming Caps, window film, or other tools to reduce visual overstimulation*
- *Sound-masking options to drown out stressful sounds outside*

Security
- Limiting or eliminating exposure to stressors until the dog has skills to navigate those stressors
- *Creating a safe space for your dog*
- *Teaching your dog to move away from stressors*

Species-typical behaviors
- *Tug*
- Flirt pole
- *Fetch*
- *Digging pits*
- *K9 Nosework, scatter feeding, sniffaris, snuffle mats*
- *Food puzzles*
- Dog sports
- *Chew toys*

Foraging
- *K9 Nosework, scatter feeding, sniffaris, snuffle mats*
- *Food puzzles*

Social interaction
- *Snuggle time with your dog!*
- *Play and outings with your dog*
- *Doggie dates for dogs who enjoy one or two friends*
- *Playgroups, dog daycares, or dog parks for dogs who are social butterflies*

Mental stimulation
- *Some kinds of training*
- *Food puzzles at the appropriate difficulty level*
- Some dog sports

Calming
- *Relaxation protocols that create conditions for a dog to relax on their own and put it on cue rather than trying to force relaxation by controlling body position*
- *Designated rest periods*
- *An environment that facilitates rest*
- *Discuss if pet is a candidate for anti-anxiety medication with a veterinary behaviorist or qualified veterinarian*

Independence
- *Providing choices and teaching your dog how to make choices on their own*
- Teaching your dog how to be comfortable being alone

Environment
- *Creating a space that reduces stressors, provides opportunities for rest, exploration, and play, and enables the dog to move freely between spaces and either solicit or retreat from social interaction as desired*

Step 5: Prioritize activities
Recall from Step 2 that the categories that kept coming up were security, environment, and calming. Because of that, anything in those categories has a higher priority.

Physical exercise prioritization
- If necessary: Games like tug, fetch, and hide and seek
- If necessary: Playing with other dogs

Sensory stimulation prioritization
- Across the Board: Scent games like scent tubes, scatter feeding, or K9 Nosework
- If necessary: Sniffaris
- If necessary: Massage, T-Touch, Jin Shin Jyutsu, etc.
- If necessary: Texture, food, or toy preference tests
- Small Step Big Win: Visual masking via Calming Caps, window film, or other tools to reduce visual overstimulation
- Small Step Big Win: Sound masking options to drown out stressful sounds outside

Security
- Laying the Foundation & Building: Creating a safe space for your dog
- Laying the Foundation & Building: Teaching your dog to move away from stressors

Species-typical behaviors
- If necessary: Tug
- If necessary: Fetch
- If necessary: Digging pits
- Across the Board: K9 Nosework, scatter feeding, sniffaris, snuffle mats
- Laying the Foundation: Food puzzles
- If necessary: Chew toys

Foraging
- Across the Board: K9 Nosework, scatter feeding, sniffaris, snuffle mats
- Laying the Foundation: Food puzzles

Social interaction
- If necessary: Snuggle time with your dog!
- If necessary: Play and outings with your dog
- If necessary: Doggie dates for dogs who enjoy one or two friends
- If necessary: Playgroups, dog daycares, or dog parks for dogs who are social butterflies

Mental stimulation
- Laying the Foundation: Some kinds of training
- Laying the Foundation: Food puzzles at the appropriate difficulty level

Calming
- Laying the Foundation & Building: Relaxation protocols that create conditions for a dog to relax on their own and put it on cue rather than trying to force relaxation by controlling body position
- Small Step Big Win: Designated rest periods
- Small Step Big Win: An environment that facilitates rest
- Across the Board: Discuss if pet is a candidate for anti-anxiety medication with a veterinary behaviorist or qualified veterinarian

Independence
- Laying the Foundation & Building: Providing choices and teaching your dog how to make choices on their own

Environment
- Across the Board, Laying the Foundation, Building: Creating a space that reduces stressors, provides opportunities for rest, exploration, and play, and enables the dog to move freely between spaces and either solicit or retreat from social interaction as desired

Note for Ruby's priorities: Her parents had already started training with her and only needed minor tweaks to her management plan (within what was reasonable). That means we were able to start on some Laying the Foundation tasks sooner than would be possible in other cases.

Aspect of Enrichment	Is this need being met?	Agency?	Priority
Health/Veterinary	Likely	Room for Growth	
Hygiene	Likely	Room for Growth	
Diet/Nutrition	Likely	Appropriate	
Physical Exercise	Potential Room for Growth	Appropriate	
Sensory Stimulation	Room for Growth	Appropriate	2.1: Window film and sound masking 1.1: Find it
Safety	Likely	Appropriate	
Security	Room for Growth	Room for Growth	1.1: Antianxiety medication 3.1: Teach her to eat food that's thrown to her 3.2: Look at That outside to man
Instinctual Behaviors	Potential Room for Growth	Potential Room for Growth	1.1: Find it
Foraging	Room for Growth	Appropriate	1.1: Find it
Social Interaction	Room for Growth	Room for Growth	3.2: Look at That outside to man
Mental Exercise	Potential Room for Growth	Appropriate	1.1: Find it
Independence	Room for Growth	Room for Growth	
Environment	Room for Growth	Room for Growth	2.1: Window film and sound masking
Calming	Room for Growth	Room for Growth	1.1: Medication 3.1: Relaxation protocol when man not present

How much is too much?

Hold up. You said to only try one thing at a time. THIS IS A LOT OF THINGS. What gives? Yes, you're right in that we're breaking our own rules here. That's because we've worked with a lot of cases like Ruby and we know when and how to break the rules. We have a pretty good idea of how most of this is going to work and how these different components usually work together. We're comfortable breaking the rule when we think it's merited, and if we're wrong, then going back to the drawing board and working more methodically. Plus, Ruby's parents were not brand new to training and already had some necessary skills under their belt so we could move faster than with a completely green handler. In this case, we felt that breaking the rules was merited because of how much chronic stress Ruby was experiencing every day. She needed as close to immediate relief as we could provide. She responded in the way that we expected (as you'll see in a future step).

Step 6: Develop a Plan of Action

- Who
  - Human preference for implementing
  - Dog preference for implementing
- What
  - What one thing we're testing
  - What our goals are
  - What we're using to measure progress
- When
  - Time of day
  - Duration
  - How long we'll try it for
- Where
  - Physical location
  - Types of situations

Aspect of Enrichment	Is this need being met?	Agency?	Priority	Plan of Action
Health/Veterinary	Likely	Room for Growth		
Hygiene	Likely	Room for Growth		
Diet/Nutrition	Likely	Appropriate		
Physical Exercise	Potential Room for Growth	Appropriate		
Sensory Stimulation	Room for Growth	Appropriate	2.1: Window film and sound masking	Who: Dad will install What: decreased sound sensitivity, increased rest (see previous sidebar about testing multiple things) When: for as long as necessary Where: front room, loudest times of day
			1.1: Find it	Who: Mom What: able to take food off floor, decreased attention-seeking behaviors, increase rest When: after work, 10 minutes, 3x/week Where: front room, kitchen, outside, only when she's capable of learning/eating
Safety	Likely	Appropriate		

Aspect of Enrichment	Is this need being met?	Agency?	Priority	Plan of Action
Security	Room for Growth	Room for Growth	1.1: Medication	Who: Mom will call vet What: medication protocol per vet, increased rest, decreased pacing When: call tomorrow Where: [vet clinic name redacted for client confidentiality
			3.1: Teach her to eat food that's thrown to her	Who: Mom What: consistently eats tossed food When: daily, 2-3 min, throughout day Where: inside house and outside, no distractions
			3.2: Look at That outside to man	Who: Mom handling, Dad at distance What: be able to decrease distance comfortably When: every other day, <5 min Where: in yard, low distractions
Instinctual Behaviors	Potential Room for Growth	Potential Room for Growth	1.1: Find it	See above
Foraging	Room for Growth	Appropriate	1.1: Find it	See above
Social Interaction	Room for Growth	Room for Growth	3.2: Look at That outside to man	See above
Mental Exercise	Potential Room for Growth	Appropriate	1.1: Find it	See above
Independence	Room for Growth	Room for Growth		
Environment	Room for Growth	Room for Growth	2.1: Window film and sound masking	See above

63

Aspect of Enrichment	Is this need being met?	Agency?	Priority	Plan of Action
Calming	Room for Growth	Room for Growth	1.1: Medication	See above
			3.1: Relaxation protocol when man not present	Who: Mom What: RP on mat in living room, increased relaxation on mat When: every other day for as long as she's successful Where: mat in living room, Dad not present

Note: The duration of implementation for this phase was two weeks — essentially, the time between the first and second sessions.

Step 7: Implement and document

Note for this section: Allie worked with Ruby before she started using progress logs with private, pet-owning clients and she doesn't remember every detail that would be necessary to go into this precise of an example. What's included in this step is completely made up to showcase the most pressing issue — being fearful of the man in the house — while following the overall trajectory of Ruby's case.

Intensity Chart

1: Settles but doesn't relax when Dad is present

2: Pacing behind couch

3: Growling at Dad

4: Won't come out of crate

The multiple numbers on each day represent notations of Ruby's behavior at different times during the day.

	Monday	Tuesday	Wednesday	Thursday	Friday	Saturday	Sunday
Week 1	4, 2, 2, 3	4, 2, 3, 3	4, 2	2, 3, 2	4, 3, 2	2, 2, 2	3, 2, 3, 1
Week 2	3, 2, 2	2, 1	2, 2, 1	2, 3	4, 3, 2	3, 2, 2, 1	2, 2, 1

Step 8: Reassess, readdress, and do it again

Ruby's family saw progress in all aspects of the categories and activities we started her with, and she had started a medication protocol per her vet. Dad was having less difficulty caring for her throughout the day and she would now eat food that he threw to her thanks to Mom laying that foundation. They were able to move on to the next step with almost all exercises.

They were, however, having difficulty with the Look at That exercise as it was difficult to find times where they were both home and there was little distraction outside. We tweaked a few aspects of this exercise, which worked better for them in the following weeks.

Of course, at each subsequent session, Allie was reassessing and readdressing the enrichment plan in her head to ensure they continued on in this trajectory. But this first pass gives you an idea of how the process works.

Blank Worksheets

Pages 66 through 71 contain blank worksheets for your use.

- Desierable and Undesirable List
- Are Needs Being Met Checklist
- Enrichment Chart
- Agency Flowchart

Desirable & Undesirable Behaviors

List desirable and undesirable behaviors

Current/existing desirable behaviors:	Current/existing undesirable behaviors:
•	•
•	•
•	•
•	•
•	•
•	•
•	•
Goal behaviors:	•
•	•
•	•
•	•
•	•
•	•
•	•
•	•

"Are Needs Being Met"
Checklist

Health/Veterinary

- ☐ Regular vet visits
- ☐ Up to date on vaccinations or the equivalent
- ☐ Pain management if needed
- ☐ Management for physical and mental health concerns: medication, physical therapy, surgery, etc.

Hygiene (remember that this is dependent on breed/ morphology)

- ☐ Appropriate amount of bathing
- ☐ Appropriate skin & coat care
- ☐ Ear cleaning
- ☐ Nail trims
- ☐ Dental hygiene
- ☐ Other breed-specific hygiene practices

Diet/Nutrition

- ☐ Appropriate diet for the individual, no health concerns
- ☐ Treats for different scenarios

Physical Exercise

- ☐ Amount of physical activity appreciably reduces fidgeting and other boredom-based behaviors
- ☐ Type of exercise does not compromise physical or mental health (e.g., exacerbates joint disease, causes distress, etc.)

Sensory Stimulation

- ☐ The environment does not elicit stress responses the majority of the time
- ☐ Absence of stereotypical behaviors
- ☐ Opportunities for behavioral diversity

Safety

- ❏ Does not have access to poisonous foods, medications, plants, household items
- ❏ Is not able to interact with animals who would cause bodily or psychological harm, including domestic species, predators, and wildlife
- ❏ Is not able to run into the street or other harmful environments
- ❏ Is not able to interact with humans who would cause bodily or psychological harm
- ❏ Is not exposed to harmful husbandry and training methods and tools

Security

- ❏ Has at least one space in their environment to retreat to where they are exposed to minimal stressors
- ❏ Knows how to move away from stressors when necessary
- ❏ Knows how to investigate novel stimuli
- ❏ Displays fear- or avoidance-related behaviors only in response to reasonable, novel, and/or extraordinary stimuli

Species-Typical/Instinctual Behaviors (including but not limited to: chewing, shredding, digging, barking, chasing, investigating, scavenging, etc.)

- ❏ Has opportunities to display species- or breed-typical behaviors in healthy, safe, and appropriate ways
- ❏ Appropriate species- or breed-typical behaviors are performed with enough frequency and diversity so as to reduce nuisance behaviors

Foraging

- ❏ Knows how to track and/or trail scents
- ❏ Knows how to problem solve in manipulating objects to obtain food
- ❏ The majority of their caloric intake is consumed via foraging
- ❏ Has daily opportunities to perform above behaviors

Social Interaction

- ❏ Is able to interact with individuals (relative to their level of sociability) in healthy, safe, and appropriate ways
- ❏ Is not forced to interact with distressing individuals and/or species
- ❏ Is able to display a diversity of behaviors in the presence of others
- ❏ Displays appropriate play solicitation behaviors, including breaks and self-regulation

Mental Exercise

- ❏ Regular opportunities to learn new or expand on existing skills
- ❏ Regular opportunities to track and/or trail scents
- ❏ Regular opportunities to problem solve

Independence

- ❏ Is able to self-entertain
- ❏ Displays no or minimal distress signals when left alone
- ❏ Is able to problem solve situations with minimal human guidance
- ❏ Is able to appropriately communicate needs

Environment

❏ Is provided with predictability, including a predictable schedule/ routines, predictable outcomes, and a reasonably predictable environment (the level of predictability necessary is relative to the individual, based on overall behavioral health)

❏ Regular access to basic necessities

❏ Regular access to opportunities for species-typical behaviors and behavioral diversity

❏ Minimal exposure to chronic or acute stressors

Calming

❏ Takes midday naps

❏ Sleeps soundly at night

❏ Is able to relax in well-known environments

❏ Is able to self-soothe and self-regulate

Enrichment Chart

Aspect of Enrichment	Is this need being met?	Is There Agency?	Priority	Plan of Action
Health/Veterinary				
Hygiene				
Diet/Nutrition				
Physical Exercise				
Sensory Stimulation				
Safety				
Security				
Species-Typical Behaviors				
Foraging				
Social Interaction				
Mental Exercise				
Independence				
Environment				
Calming				

Agency Flowchart

Does Your Pet Have Agency?

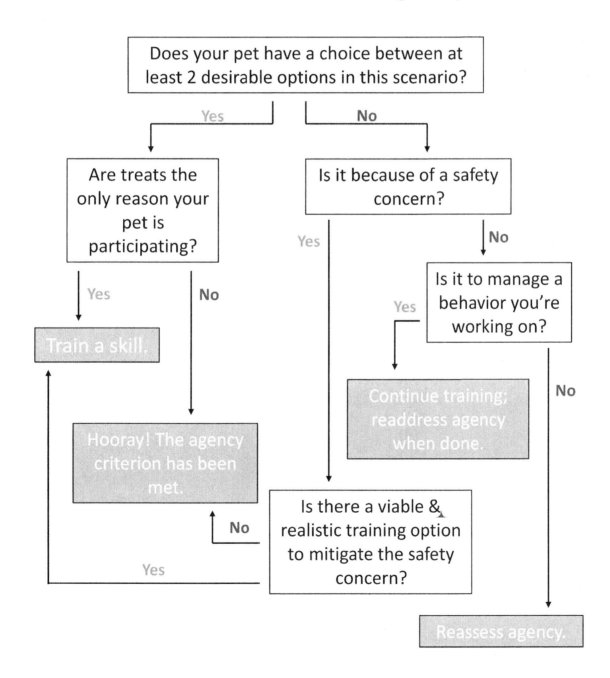

Dogwise.com is your source for quality books, ebooks, DVDs, training tools and treats.

We've been selling to the dog fancier for more than 25 years and we carefully screen our products for quality information, safety, durability and FUN! You'll find something for every level of dog enthusiast on our website, www.dogwise.com, or drop by our store in Wenatchee, Washington.

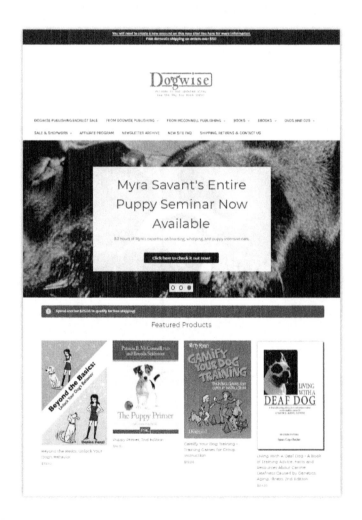

Printed in Great Britain
by Amazon

46508408R00044